Change a little
to change a lot

Karen Ward, energy therapist from the BBC's *The Last Resort* and holistic therapy presenter from RTÉ's highly successful programme *Health Squad*, is co-author of the best-selling book *The Health Squad Guide to Health and Fitness*. With an honours science degree from UCD, Karen now works as a holistic psychotherapist, stress management counsellor and energy therapist from her clinic in Smithfield, Dublin. She is an established lecturer and facilitator of motivational and inspiring talks on a variety of holistic health subjects. Karen and her husband, John Cantwell, teach and run a school of shamanism – holistic living called 'Slí an Chroí'. She treats all her treasured clients from a mind, body, spirit and energetic perspective. www.karenwardholistictherapist.com

Change a little
to change a lot

KAREN WARD

MERLIN

PUBLISHING

First published in 2009 by
Merlin Publishing
Newmarket Hall, Cork Street,
Dublin 8, Ireland
Tel: +353 1 4535866
Fax: +353 1 4535930
publishing@merlin.ie
www.merlinwolfhound.com

13-Digit ISBN 978-1-903582-91-6

A CIP catalogue record for this book is available from the
British Library.

10 9 8 7 6 5 4 3 2 1

Typesetting, layout and cover design: Claire McVeigh
Printed and bound by CPI Cox & Wyman, Britain
Cover image courtesy of Getty Images/ Rosemary Calvert
Front cover author image courtesy of Rhyna McCarthy
Illustration of The Chakra System on page 29 reproduced with
kind permission from Pam Ward © Pam Ward

Acknowledgements

There are many people I would like to thank for their help and support over the years: my beloved Aunt Anne, who has always been there for me, as have the magnifique Di Pizzos, Jackie and Jim Sheehan 'xx', wonderful Wardie Greg, the inspirational Ward Pratts, Powerful Pam Ward and gorgeous George Parkes. The extended Ward and Whitty Clans. Also, Agnes, her late husband Frank and all the marvellous Cantwells, who welcomed me wholeheartedly into their families.

My 'cuddies' – Sea Goddess, Sherrie Scott; Sky Goddess, Eimear Burke and Wonder Woman, María Jesús López, for their unconditional love and support. My chum, John Dick, who was a true gentleman. Aoife and Fiona O'Grady – two beautiful princesses. Sterre Pol, my little shining star.

Chenile Keogh and Robert Doran at Merlin Publishing. Also thanks to Síne Quinn and Claire McVeigh. Mario Diciotti and Pinella Matta in Sardinia; your hospitality while writing this book was perfect. Catherine O'Connor – a friend who always runs that extra mile. My fabulous *Health Squad* buddies: Paula Mee, Padraig Murphy and Sheana Keane. Oliver McCabe – networker extraordinaire!

All the inspirational clients and students I have had the privilege of working with over the years – buíochas libh go léir. The ever increasing Slí an Chroí Tuatha. Mother Earth and all her bounty, Father Sky and my spiritual family and ancestors.
Dia dhúinn go deo.

Contents

Introduction

This book is a tried and tested guide on how to cope with the ups and downs of life. It is wisdom from one Irish woman who has lived 46 years, and has come to the holistic way of being through trial and error to a place of inner peace, love and knowing. My sincerest wish is to share what I have learnt with you, offering simple, practical advice on living in our busy modern world naturally, while enjoying life to the full.

How many times do we overwhelm ourselves by trying to change too many things about ourselves all at the same time? This probably happens every New Year, at the start of the summer holidays or when we are thinking of buying that little black number for the Christmas party. We are inadvertently setting ourselves up for failure, which can lead us to feel disheartened, and then we give up completely. Often we can feel that the mountain is just too high to scale and we'll never reach the top. Rather than setting out to climb Everest, I'm suggesting we gently stroll over the Hill of Tara and when we are done and feel great, set out again for another hill around the same size.

Change a Little to Change a Lot is a hands-on guide to restoring balance to your busy lifestyle. I want to show you how the holistic approach to improving your life need not be daunting. Packed with simple and easy to follow tips, the book reveals how to listen to your body, mind and spirit, and really hear what it is trying to tell you. By changing one thing at a time, and really focusing on it, you are much more likely to succeed in creating the life you want. That way you can achieve a sustainable rhythm, by building on these practical steps and maintaining their practice.

I often use storytelling when I work with clients to illustrate a point. I guess it is my bardic genes coming out. The next story sums up the whole premise of this book and was the inspiration for me to write it. The woman is a mix and match of a number of different clients with a huge dollop of me in there as well.

The Hairy Carpet Tile Story

There was a woman who had an overgrown garden, which she saw every time she washed her dishes, as it faced her kitchen window. She was feeling very low in herself and felt that everything was hopeless in her life at that time. This depressing view she felt was a visual reminder of her plight. She had no one to help her, and everyone who saw her garden further compounded the problem by remarking on how 'it looks like a jungle', 'you'll never be able to clear that'. One day, in a fit of pique, she took a kitchen fork and a hairy carpet tile and went into the garden. She measured up a square of weeds, exactly the same size as the tile, and started to dig. Then she stopped. The next day she moved onto the next square patch, again measuring it to the same size as the tile. Her neighbours and friends laughed at her. However, she continued each day, only doing one tile, but tending the patches she had already dug too. In one month she had her garden, her self-esteem and her motivation in life back. The hairy carpet tile changed her life. I tell this story to my clients to highlight how often small changes can lead to overall big changes in life.

Change a Little to Change a Lot **gives you a number of small approachable and achievable ways to** make a larger impact on your life. May this book contribute in some small way to changing yours.

A Pratical Tip

To get the most out of this book, use a fancy notebook or journal for the various exercises I have outlined in each chapter. I also give holistic tips, and you may like to write down how you feel when you have tried them. Keep the notebook and the book together, so you will be ready to continue the adventure, at a moments notice, as the mood grabs you.

Chapter *1*
Change

Let's get something straight from the beginning: change is a fact of life. Along with death it is the only guarantee we have. Now that does sound a bit scary but I realised that once we come to terms with it, life, including change, becomes a lot easier. Change is a form of ending which leads to new beginnings – a natural life cycle. I've accepted that the 'in tray' will always be full, so now I can settle down to pace myself to a rhythm of working, family and social living that is sustainable. Of course, I realise that once I have settled into a rhythm of life that suits the age I am at now, guess what? I'll grow older and have to adapt, once again, to my new age and all that it brings in terms of physical, mental and lifestyle change. I can't turn back the clock, but I can be wise enough to flow along with age, celebrating each milestone as it comes. Long ago I came to the conclusion that fighting it was futile. However, I also sussed that giving up and surrendering to decrepitude was defeatist too. So a healthy combination of good food, stimulating exercise, lots of love and friendship is the route for me. I'd like to share with you what I have learnt.

Your Personal NCT

In our modern world, we often look after our cars better than our bodies. We bring them to their bi-yearly NCT, and lovingly fill them with the best fuel and oil. Do we treat our bodies in the same way? Not often. Once we pass 40, it is a very good idea to get a regular check-up with our local doctor. I suggest at least every two years – using our NCT as a reminder. It really is no big deal – it's simply part of looking after yourself. If there was a problem at work or home wouldn't we want to know about it? To have the whole picture rather than thinking there is something hidden? Early detection means we CAN do something about it. Women should have regular smear tests and breast checks, and men should have regular prostate gland tests. These may not be the most pleasant experiences but they are nothing to be frightened of. Remember, it is our responsibility alone to look after our body. Not even the richest person in the world can pay someone to exercise or lose weight for them. Sting gets up early each morning to do his yoga. Gwyneth Paltrow eats macrobiotic food. We are forever hearing about the healthy habits of countless celebrities. By now, we know that the sensible lifestyles work and the faddy lifestyles don't. We only have to look at any magazine stand to see in glorious colour both the good and bad effects.

Personally, I go to my doctor every two years, and on the alternate year I get my eyes, teeth, back and feet checked. You may think this is too much but I have been amazed at the difference two years can make to my health once over forty. I look after myself, so you can imagine the changes that might have occurred if I didn't.

Holistic Tip
Your Personal Health File

Keep all your health records in one place.

This is a good idea for many reasons. Firstly, you can see how your health is doing by checking up on previous records. Your doctor will also keep a record, but you may change doctor or need to keep information on different health care professionals handy. This way you can know at a glance how your cholesterol, blood pressure, bone density, etc., is doing every time you do your personal NCT. Secondly, your next of kin may need to know in case of an accident. Thirdly, you will have a reference for when you had the last tests done.

The Red Flag

Often we plod along through the various phases of our life literally going through the motions. Until some day, seemingly out of the blue, something goes wrong. This may be physical, mental or emotional. Your body is the house of your soul. It is like a snail's shell – your temple. Ideally you want it to be a well-oiled machine with a happy, healthy mind, emotions you respond to and a sense of purpose to your life. However, perhaps, like all of us, you sometimes forget that you reap what you sow. I call these out of the blue problems 'red flags', signalling danger. It is time to stop and figure out what is wrong and how to right it.

What would happen if we all stopped breathing right now? We'd die straight away. If we stopped eating and drinking how long would we last? A week? What about if we stop relaxing or exercising? It could be weeks or months until eventually something will go wrong. Usually it is our body's weak point. Each of us has a different one, and because there is a gap between not relaxing or exercising – the problem is we don't associate the two. Therefore we don't realise the effect of the lack of them but our bodies do.

So let's do a little survey. In your notebook write down any of the following, if they occur frequently for you. Classic physical weak point symptoms are: headaches and migraines, neck and shoulder aches, tense shoulders, asthma, frequent colds, stomach ulcers, IBS, constipation, diarrhoea, recurring back and knee injuries. Then there are the mental and emotional weak points that we don't usually talk about: worrying, depression, panic attacks, low self-esteem, anger, frustration and tears.

If your body is trying to tell you something ... listen! In fact your weak point, which might be hereditary or due to an accident/repeated strain, could be your best friend. Whatever you have written down is your own personal red flag. Every time it plays up – STOP and look for the reason why. Usually it is lack of sleep, unwise food choices, worry and stress. By being aware of your red flags and changing what is causing them, you can improve your general well being.

Holistic Tip
Family Red Flags

Look at the list of physical, emotional and mental red flags you wrote down, and rate them in order of frequent occurrence. Now write down anything you know about the health conditions of your parents and grandparents, including what they may have died from.

Being aware of your family's health is important for understanding the potential physical red flags you might have. Interestingly, most people just seem to know that granny passed away, but aren't sure what she died of: stroke, heart attack, etc. It is actually very important to note this family information, because if you know what conditions exist in your lineage then you can do something about them now, before it is too late. I have heart conditions, bowel and throat cancer in my family health history. I don't smoke, eat well and look after my stress levels. I need to, my father died from a heart attack at 53. I realised that there's no point in me waiting until I'm 50 to do something about it — I need to act now. So figure out what is going on in your family tree, then make those preventative health steps now.

The Holistic Approach

This is looking at the big picture – the whole story. The term 'holistic' may be relatively new, but the use of it has been around for centuries in many, many forms of healing and medical work. We know from ancient Indian, Greek and Chinese texts that the human body has been treated for prevention, maintenance and ill health from a mind, body and spirit perspective. We also know from indigenous people the world over, who are still using holistic therapies that if we treat a problem we have a cure, but if we get to its source, and gain understanding, then we have healing.

If someone with a tense neck and shoulders gets massage therapy they will receive relief for a few days. However, if they understand that their hectic work and family schedule, plus not getting enough time to themselves is exacerbating the problem, then they can do something about it. Nowadays, there is an increasing awareness of the need to take responsibility for our own health, and prevention is the key strategy. Unfortunately in Ireland, our health system is currently overloaded. If we all took better care of ourselves and became more aware of holistic approaches, as well as traditional medical care, this would help the current health care situation. Many medical centres are now set up around the country with a mix of both, which is a progressive step towards improving our health care.

Holistic Tip
Keep it Simple

If you recognise that there is something in your life that you need to change, first acknowledge what it is. Then write out simple steps in your notebook that will lead to the goal you have chosen. Finally, do ONLY one step at a time or you run the risk of completely overloading yourself. This is a recipe for disaster and is the reason why many of us fail to make any significant personal health changes in our lives. Literally take one manageable step at a time, stick to it then when it is part of your life, take the next logical step.

Laughter is the Best Medicine

I once had the fortuitous opportunity to visit the ancient sacred city of Machu Picchu in Peru. During our visit, I ended up in the Temple of the Moon at a ceremony with an elder of the Q'ero South American Indian people. It was a most auspicious occasion, and my husband, John, and I were thrilled to be there with our wonderful friends, Kay and Ann. Don Sebastian was the chief celebrant. Suddenly, in the middle of the ritual, he stopped and spoke strongly to our friend, guide and translator, Dennis. We were baffled. What was going on? Was this normal? The explanation was unbelievable. He explained that we were all much too serious and pious and that we had to take a break and lighten up! So, I ended up on this magnificent site doing the hokey cokey, and crying with laughter. Once he was satisfied that we were 'ourselves' and were open to receiving the wisdom of the ceremony, Don Sebastian continued. What a lesson it was for us that day. How often do we mould ourselves into the way we think we should be in given situations, losing our childlike playfulness?

Chapter 2
Weight Loss

Weight Loss Secrets for Life

As we get older our body's requirements change. Our metabolic rate slows down to accommodate the aging process. As a result of this change it can be harder to lose weight. With each decade gained our bodies require a different exercise plan, and the need for healthy eating increases. Becoming aware of our body's changes helps us understand that it is unrealistic for a forty-year-old woman to expect to have the body of a nineteen-year-old. With the right care some women may even look better in their forties than they did as teenagers.

Listening to our bodies is always a good starting point in order to lose weight and keep the weight off. We need to tune in to our body systems and go with the very valuable information they give us on a daily basis, for example, have you ever noticed that when you eat certain foods you feel hyperactive or tired or even a bit nauseous? In our busy world we usually don't notice these things, but the signs are always there. Imagine a team of little men and women who run your digestive system. They LOVE when you eat fruit and vegetables and wholesome simple foods. They DON'T LIKE when you eat processed, heavy, fatty, sugary food. They will tell you when they are not happy with signals like: indigestion, acid stomach, bloating, flatulence, constipation or diarrhoea. So, rather than wait until your 'mini digestive team' gives you a huge warning sign like obesity, diverticulitus or ulcers, why not pay attention to the small signs that you can change one at a time.

As well as feeling better you will look better, as healthy eating improves your skin tone, strengthens your nails and can even add shine to your hair – as well as giving an extra sparkle to your eyes. Of course the energy boost you gain from healthy eating is of major importance, as this gives you the impetus to continue, especially when you reach the dreaded plateau for a few weeks, as your body and skin acclimatise to the new changes.

It really is surprising how much we can eat in one day without realising it. It is a good idea to make a record of your eating, just to see how much you eat without being aware of it. Times to look out for are: tasting the food as you are cooking, snack times and the late night supper time. If you ever watch the many television programmes about weight loss, you will have seen a version of this in action.

Holistic Tip
Food & Mood Diary

In your notebook jot down everything you eat and drink for three days. Half an hour later, note how your mood is and what messages your body has told you. This is where you can bring your emotions and physical reactions into your weight loss regime.

This vital information will help you to know what foods agree and – more importantly – don't agree with you. If you do this tip once a month, by the end of six months you will know which foods nourish your system on a daily basis, and which foods are purely treat foods to be eaten only once or twice a week.

Realistic Role Models

Most of us aspire to be like people we admire for different reasons: their accomplishments, their talent or their style. It is a great idea to have these so-called role models. Often it might be a film star or musician, perhaps a sports man or woman. However, it would be a major step to look or behave like these people. Madonna does a two-hour Ashtanga yoga workout six days a week and David Beckham trains for hours every day. It is fabulous to aim to look like them, but to sustain that type of exercise regime in our daily routine could be too much for most of us mere mortals. So we'd give up or just assume it would be way too hard to achieve. We'd feel like failures, and perhaps comfort ourselves by then eating all the wrong foods or do no exercise at all.

Holistic Tip
Small Manageable Steps

Why not pick realistic role models, like the man next door who walks the dog every evening or the woman who does the yoga class near work every Wednesday lunchtime. Take small manageable steps that are achievable. Keep it going, until it becomes part of your daily routine, then move onto a new step. You'll feel a terrific sense of progress quite quickly, which will spur you on.

Routine, Routine, Routine

We are creatures of habit whether we like it or not. Generally we work and sleep seven to eight hours a day, and eat three meals. If we constantly change our daily habits it is very difficult to maintain a healthy eating regime. Our mealtimes are anchors in our busy world – a time to relax, enjoy and socialise. If you skip meals then your 'mini digestive team' will give you cravings to eat sugary quick-fix foods as a survival mechanism. Ever wondered why you don't lose weight when you skip breakfast? Your body goes into famine mode and you then end up snacking.

Holistic Tip
Relish Your Food

So when was the last time you actually sat down with family or friends and enjoyed a meal without the television in the background? Do you eat in the car/at your desk? Try sitting down for at least one meal a day to start. Make a date with a friend or family member to catch up on news, or read something as a way of helping you take this valuable time to relish your food. Once you have one meal sorted then move onto the next one, until all three meals are times you look forward to.

Exercise and Healthy Eating as a Team

The best way to tone up and get fit is to combine exercise and healthy eating. Think of a way you can exercise for either three hours or six half hours a week. Be imaginative – set dancing, salsa and badminton count too. I use the maxim 'Is it worth it?', when I'm about to eat anything that isn't good for me or skip an exercise class. Usually my answer is 'No, it isn't'. Sometimes it will be worth it. Granny's chocolate cake, which was lovingly made, may actually be better for you than a shop-bought apple – as long as it is a one off treat and not every day.

The older we get the less food we need. However, by the time this happens we are used to eating a certain amount. Add this to a more sedentary lifestyle and the weight piles on. This information might explain why the extra pounds suddenly have crept up, even though we are eating and exercising the same amount as before. They don't call it middle-age spread for nothing!

Instead of moaning about the extra weight, decide if you would prefer to cut out some treats or exercise more. If not, stop moaning – your family love you as you are!

Metabolism Explained

As we get older our metabolic rate decreases, therefore we don't need the same amount of calories. A woman's calorie requirements, depending on height and body type, change from: approximately 2,000 a day at forty; 1,900 at fifty; down to 1,800 at seventy. A man's calorie requirements change from: approximately 2,500 a day at fifty; 2,350 at sixty; down to 2,100 at seventy.

Pleasure/Pain Principle

Every day at some point we experience both pleasure and pain. If we didn't have pain then we wouldn't know what pleasure is. However, the level of pain and pleasure is down to us. Many of us spend our lives trying to hold onto the pleasure, thus avoiding the pain at all costs. So here's something to try to ease both, free up your energy and help you sail through your day with equanimity. Why not embrace the pain and choose what it's going to be. I can choose to get up earlier than usual (self-chosen controlled pain) and start my day's work relaxed and ready, rather than experience pain later on, by being stressed when I don't get everything done on time ('out of the blue' uncontrolled pain). Then I will have the guaranteed pleasure of feeling good when my day starts on a roll. I can choose to exercise (the self-controlled pain of getting started) rather than experience the pain of feeling unfit, fatigued or fat later on ('out of the blue' uncontrolled pain). If I choose the self-controlled pain, I am guaranteed the pleasure of feeling virtuous having finished my exercise.

Many clients seem surprised when I share that sometimes I find it difficult to get to an exercise class. They assume that because I know the benefits that it is easy for me to go. I use the affirmation (a soothing positive sentence), 'Just get to the class, Karen, get to the class', murmured over and over again, as I prepare to go, as a way to ensure I get there and do what I know is good for me.

Holistic Tip
Do Something Positive Now

If you feel negative about yourself, because you are overweight or unfit or tired, that thought can spiral down until you're in a bad mood. Then you will definitely not exercise and will probably comfort eat. So, when you feel the first small negative thought creep in immediately DO SOMETHING POSITIVE NOW. You could drink water, listen to music, ring a friend or do some exercise. Then the negative thought goes away, and you will feel better, as you have done something positive towards good health.

Comfort Eating

I once had a client who was obese, a lovely woman that had tried many different ways to lose weight. She came to me as a last resort. At first, she told me all about what she had tried and how she failed. She was beating herself up for failing time and time again. I asked her why she ate so much of the wrong type of food. She looked at me absolutely stunned. 'What do you mean?', she retorted. 'What does food mean to you, especially the junk food, as you call it?' I replied.

As she thought about it, tears began to spill down her cheeks. When she was a small child her mother died, and her Gran had given her sweet treats to cheer her up. She felt solace in the sugary taste and it gave her great comfort. All through her life, whenever she had difficulties or felt even remotely sad or down she ate those foods. We then worked to allow her to process the feelings of loss around her mother's passing. The death of a parent is a huge change in anyone's life, but especially in one so young. Next, we began to outline ways she could deal with the stresses and strains of life but with natural techniques that didn't involve eating. Finally, we looked at energy foods that were a little bit exotic, like pineapple, artichokes and quinoa that made her feel special as she ate them. She turned her life around in six months, and changed her dress size from a twenty to a fourteen in a year.

Chapter *3*
Energy Boost

Most of us aren't conscious of how important our energy field is to our well being. This energy field or life force, also called our aura, is very evident in a new born baby and very noticeably absent in someone who has died.

We are all completely aware of waking up some days feeling tired, just wanting to pull the duvet back over our heads. Other days we spring out of bed full of the joys of life. I bet you have experienced meeting someone who you connect with instantly, even though you hardly know them. Perhaps, you also know what it feels like to get odd vibes from certain places for no apparent reason. We're a lot more tuned into our energy than we think. Since change is a fact of life, getting to know what consistently keeps your natural energy on a steady flow is vital. I believe that all our ills are traceable within our energy field. They leave an imbalance there that originates from a negative life experience. However, if you are under stress or have repeated negative life experiences then a build up can occur. If this is left unattended to then it can develop into a chronic emotional, mental or physical problem, as our system tries to get our attention to change our lifestyle for the better.

What is Our Energy Like?

I think of it like electricity in the sense that you know it is there, even though you can't see it. Ancient healing therapies like yoga, t'ai chi and acupuncture have mapped the human energy system into invisible lines, called meridians, throughout the body. There are seven keys areas where our energy is stored called chakras (meaning wheel in the ancient Indian language of Sanskrit, as they spin clockwise when working optimally). Each of these areas are situated along the spine to the top of the head. They are located beside and so are linked in energetically with our endocrine system, which produces the body's hormones. The ancient Irish druids called them 'The Seven Doorways'.

The Chakra System

The flow of energy in our bodies affects our physical well being. In daily life, our chakras can often become overworked and unbalanced. Our natural energy has a vibration and a frequency like all energy. Each chakra has a colour and a sound associated with it, which matches the frequency of the energy running throughout that centre. The seven colours match those of a rainbow, demonstrating the strong link between our bodies and the natural world around us. This highlights the importance of being in nature regularly to activate, energise and rebalance these important centres.

The root or base chakra is located at the pelvic floor. It is energetically linked with the reproductive organs. This chakra informs our basic survival instincts and our sense of being grounded. Its colour is red.

The sacral chakra is located below the navel. It is energetically linked with the reproductive organs and adrenal glands, which are over activated in times of stress. This chakra informs our sensuality, sexuality and ability to go with the flow. Its colour is orange.

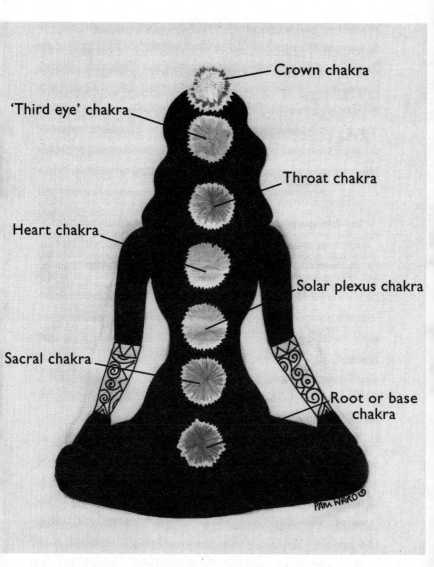

The Chakra System

The solar plexus chakra is located above the navel and below the centre of the ribs. It is energetically linked to the pancreas, which maintains our blood sugar. This chakra informs our self-esteem, confidence, sense of who we are and our purpose in the world. Its colour is yellow.

The heart chakra is located at the centre of the chest. It is energetically linked to the thymus gland, which is an important part of our immune system. This chakra informs our self-care, unconditional love and compassion. Its two colours are pastel pink and green.

The throat chakra is located at the centre of the throat. It is energetically linked to the thyroid gland, which governs our metabolism. This chakra informs our expression, willpower and communication. Its colour is blue.

The 'third eye' chakra is located between the eyebrows and above the nose. It is so called, because at night when we dream with our eyes closed we 'see' images through this part of the body. This chakra informs the integration of our subconscious, creativity, imagination and intuition. Its colour is purple.

Finally, our *crown chakra* is located above the top of the head, at what was our fontanel (visible in new babies before it closes up). It relates to our pinal gland, which is light sensitive. It informs the development of our spiritual connection whatever that might be. Its colour is pure white light.

If your energy system is flagging through stress, you can boost it by doing either an active exercise, like walking in the park, or a passive treatment, like massage, which naturally stimulates the chakras to spin clockwise and in tempo with each other. Why not try these or a specific energy exercise or treatment like yoga or acupuncture to experience how it effects your energy system positively.

Wonderful Water – A Simple Solution

Our bodies are made of approximately 70 per cent water, yet most of us don't even drink half that amount per day. The effect that this has on our energy is huge. Our bodies valiently try to give us warning signs like thirst, headaches, low back ache. Mostly we ignore them and then wonder why our energy dips later in the day. I have often heard clients say they don't like the lack of taste of water, but a squeeze of lemon will rectify that. It is worth it to ease the symptoms of water shortage in the body, especially when your energy soars and symptoms of dehydration disappear. Some people can confuse thirst with hunger, and instead of getting a glass of water, might reach for an unneeded snack. So maybe the next time you feel like a snack, have a glass of water first and then wait a while to see if you really were hungry.

Holistic Tip
Water Experiment

For one week and one week only, try an important trial. Each day drink one glass of water before breakfast, lunch and dinner. Then one mid-morning, mid-afternoon and mid evening. The pre-breakfast one might be hot with lemon, to flush out your digestive system. For the last one mid-evening, you may need to gauge the best time to have this, so you aren't going to the toilet in the middle of the night. Note how you feel, especially as the week progresses. Do your energy levels increase? If I was a betting woman, I'd say the effects will be so good and the method so simple that you will keep this small but very significant change in your life.

The Healing Effects of Nature

I mentioned that if you are under stress or have repeated negative life experiences that a build up of tension and ill health can occur. These can develop into emotional, mental or physical problems. Again this is our body telling us that all is not well, and we need to change something and fast.

A very easy way to alleviate some of these problems is to go into nature in order to take time out, such as swimming in the sea, walking or gardening. These are ways for us to tune into our inner strength and calm by taking solace and inspiration from 'Big Momma' – Mother Nature herself. I have yet to meet anyone who hasn't been moved by a stunning sunset, the sight of swans flying or bright colourful autumn leaves. We need to get out into the great outdoors to literally clear the cobwebs away, leaving our energy renewed and restored. I remember having a stupid row with a loved one and flouncing outside in a huff to see two little birds fighting over a crust of bread. I thought 'What are we like?' As I went in to apologise, I was met by the other person saying sorry, having felt ridiculous when their dog looked so sad that we were rowing!

Holistic Tip
Finding Your Nature Place

Take some time to figure out where your special place in nature is. It could be your garden, a park, a mountain, a beach or a forest. You'll know it when you ask yourself where it might be, and an image of it comes to mind and instinctively feels just right. I'm sure you have stood on a beach or a mountain top, and automatically took a deep breath, almost drinking in the fresh air. Our bodies, minds and spirits respond so well and feel so refreshed by the gorgeous tranquilty of being in nature. So taking timeout in your nature place is not only psychologically good from a break point of view, but also physiologically. Give yourself the gift of a few hours break there at least once a week.

Child's Play

One of the simplest ways to raise your energy levels is to be in the company of small children or pets. Both love unconditionally and live completely 'in the now'. This means not getting caught up in the past or spiralling off into the future, but just enjoying being in the present.

So often we look after the physical needs of our children and pets, but don't actually play with them deriving fabulous fun from being in their joyous company. Often when I take my beloved nieces and nephews out for the day, their parents thank me profusely afterwards. I tell them that the pleasure was all mine to be in such beautiful infectious energy. I am thoroughly renewed by it.

Holistic Tip
Energy Diary

On a day when your energy is low, write in your notebook what you were doing in the previous 12 hours. Are you worried about something? Did you skip meals? Is a particular emotion playing up? Note on a scale of one to ten where you would rate your energy levels that day. Now what are you going to do about it? Choose something like playing with children or pets to treating yourself to an exercise class.

Energy Therapies

You may consider acupuncture, reiki or other energy treatments, like a shamanic treatment or integrated energy therapy, especially if you feel there is a build up of negative life events that are too much to handle on your own. A professional may be able to help you clear them, depending on the nature of the challenge and how ready you are to let them go. Always go to a qualified therapist, who has been working for a number of years, via a referral, phone or recognised Internet listing. Also check if your health care provider recognises them, as you might be able to claim some money back.

A King's Ransom

Once upon a time there was a King who was exhausted. He was so sick and fatigued that not even the best physicians in the land could help him. In desperation the Queen sent for the wise old woman who lived at the end of the village. She was brought to the King's bedside, and patiently heard his plight. Finally, the wise old woman said she could help him help himself. Intrigued and with a growing sense of incredulity, the King listened to her give the remedy. He was to get up every day at seven, kiss the Queen, dress and go for a five-mile ride with his kinsmen to a well in the forest. There he was to draw and drink the water and wait for 20 minutes. Then he was to return and breakfast with the Queen and their children, making sure to allow at least half an hour of playtime. He was shocked. How could he do any of this nonsense, since he was bedridden? The old woman replied, "Sire, it is the only way". After three days, he finally relented and at seven, after his kiss, he dragged himself out of bed. He had to be literally strapped onto the horse, and rode in painful silence with his men to the well. By the time he returned to the Castle, his children and the Queen watched him virtually collapse into his breakfast. Of course, the next day he was even worse with the unaccustomed exercise. However, by the end of the week, he sprang out of bed, and chatted to the men on the way to the forest. In three weeks, he was a new man governing the land as never before.

Years passed, and the wise old woman was fetched once again to the palace, this time the King was sick, worse than ever. She asked him what had happened, had he followed her instructions? Eventually, she learned the truth. One day he was too busy to go to the well, and had asked his men to fetch the 'magic' water for him. Another day, he didn't have time to play with the children. Slowly, but surely, he lost the routine she had outlined for him. "I don't understand why the sacred water isn't working anymore?", he cried. She explained that there was nothing special about the water. All the court gasped, "How had the remedy worked before?" they asked. The wise old woman smiled. "Getting up at the same time everyday gave you routine, a kiss with the Queen brought love into your day. The ride to the forest and the 20 minutes gave you friendship and time to chat, while digesting ordinary water, necessary for our well being. Finally, eating breakfast with your family and playtime, set you up for your working day. All of these TOGETHER, your Majesty, make the magic."

Chapter *4*
Spring Clean

If we are going to make changes in our lives we need to begin by also making changes to our surroundings. So, let's start with the basics. A cluttered living space equates to a cluttered mind. It is very difficult to make any sort of new habit from a place of chaos. If your home is a constant reminder of what you need to do (put up more shelves, clean out the cupboards, recycle bottles) then it will be very difficult to have time to be creative or even relax. We are becoming more aware of the importance of our environment and the effect it has on our physical, emotional, mental and spiritual well being, so it is also important to look at the environment inside our homes.

As well as having an impact on our well being, a cluttered space can zap us of energy too. So, it is also very relevant to look at the spiritual and energetic aspects. Many of us have heard about the Chinese practice called Feng Shui or the Indian version called Vastu Vidya. Feng Shui means 'wind and water' in Chinese. It is the art of living life in harmony with nature and our man-made environment. The Indian version called Vastu Vidya, which means 'dwelling science', is the sacred practice of designing, building and decorating the home in harmony with the environment bringing health, wealth and happiness. The main principles contain the common sense elements of our traditional spring clean, which are quite simple and are very practical. They are also easy to apply to any space.

The basic concepts are to keep your living place light and spacious, so that your body and mind are also uncluttered and uplifted.

Let's look at the four main principles of spring cleaning using a living room scenario:
1. Clear out the clutter
2. Bring in light and fresh air
3. Create a restful space
4. Decorate with cheerful colours

1. Clear Out the Clutter

I imagine that every time you pass that bulging sideboard or bureau filled with old junk and rubbish you cringe slightly. In Feng Shui and Vastu Vidya terms that clutter is also in your head, and if you remove it physically from your home it will free up your thoughts. By decluttering you are freeing your mind from a constant reminder of the things you have not achieved. The clutter can be stagnating, reminding you of feeling stuck in a rut. So, removing it can allow you to enjoy life, without a visual reminder of the past.

2. Bring in Light and Fresh Air

It is good practice to open some windows and air the room every morning, even in winter for a few minutes. This lets in some fresh air to circulate around your home, and releases stale air from the previous evening. Stale air can affect your mood and can give you headaches, as well as not smelling good. The fresh air will make your room feel and smell better. (You don't need air freshener when you can just open a window.) Wind chimes are a lovely way to hear the fresh air enter your room, and can give you a lovely, almost childlike pleasure.

3. Create a Restful Space

Remove ANYTHING you associate with work from this room, if at all possible. This includes files, computers even, dare I say it, newspapers which usually have bad news. The Sunday supplements, which are usually more uplifting though, and go with relaxation time, are fine. This room should be for living in and, let's face it work-related activities are not conducive to this.

4. Decorate with Cheerful Colours

A favourite colour scheme in your living room does wonders for your mood. Obviously, you will want to make sure that your partner/family agrees with your choice. A restful calming one is best, adding a splash of deeper colour in the soft furnishings. For example, a light colour on your walls with a darker brighter colour for your sofa, cushions, curtains or blinds. Try not to have too many busy patterns or too much stuff in the room, after all, this is the main place where you chill out and relax after your busy day.

Setting the Scene

Relaxing in your living space should be a wonderful experience to be looked forward to with relish, whether it's curling up by a fire, watching an uplifting film or reading a magazine. Then you will begin to associate being in this room with peace and calm. Now that you have applied the four basic principles of spring cleaning using Feng Shui key concepts to the room, see if you notice a difference to your mood. Then see how you feel in a week. Have you noticed that you are spending more time in this room?

Holistic Tip
Clutter Clearout Time

Choose something you have been meaning to do for ages, like clearing out your kitchen cupboards/wardrobe/desk. Every day do just a small bit of clearing. Psychologically you will also be clearing the clutter from your mind, which leaves you with a sense of purpose, achievement AND motivation to make even more changes in your life. Take one room at home and decide whether to clear it out in one go or an hour a day, or even over a weekend.

Emotional Release

Before clearing out a whole room, you may need to consult with whoever else lives or lived there. Perhaps give adult children, who have moved out, a deadline to come and sort out their stuff. You could help them take it to a charity shop. Note your emotions as you go through each item. Decide whether to save it, bin it or recycle it. We often inadvertently go into 'famine/poverty mode', saving and hoarding as though there isn't enough. Energetically this attitude can show a deep insecurity that might need to be looked at with the help of a professional counsellor.

Opposites Attract

I know a couple who seemed to be a dream made in heaven for each other, until, that is, they moved in together. She always arrived for their dates looking like a beautiful doll, perfectly coiffured. His dressy casual clothes made her swoon with delight. Once they shared the same living space, he realised the absolute chaos that reigned in at least three rooms to create her look. She saw with a shock, the military precision that lead to his relaxed appearance. They had to sit down and have a major rethink on how to make their home life bearable. They turned the spare room into her 'dressing room', with two walk-in wardrobes. He agreed never to even peek in there, as the total disarray would only upset him. She agreed that he could have all the wardrobe space in their bedroom, with everything matched and folded perfectly, just the way he liked it. He had total use of the shower room ensuite, and she took the main bathroom for all her potions and lotions. They then split the cost of a weekly cleaner. Harmony was restored, and I'm happy to report they are married now and doing really well.

Is it a House or a Home?

How many houses have you ever been in that are neat and tidy, perhaps even interior-designed, but feel cold and sterile? It is important that your house is also a home that everyone, including children and teenagers, feel part of. We often hide away the children or grandchildren's toys completely or are constantly aware of our teenager's messy room. Why not come up with some creative ideas to include all members of the family, for instance, a bookshelf for your cookery/gardening books, a wall for the children's artwork, and a cabinet for any young adult's sporting trophies. If your teenager's room upsets you with its chaos – then don't go into it. Trust me, if your teenage darling wants a clean shirt or finds a mouse in their room – then they will do something about it!

Atmosphere

What is the 'sense or feel' you get intuitively when you visit someone's home? Is there a relaxed or stressed atmosphere? What do you think people feel when they enter your home? If the chief homemaker is constantly harassed or stressed, then this has an effect on the whole atmosphere of the house and its inhabitants. Remember the furnishing and the décor of the house will also reflect how everyone lives in the space. Think about the mood and atmosphere you hope to create in your home. Do you want a relaxed or energetic atmosphere? Then the interior needs to reflect your aim with subdued lighting, bookshelves, interesting or quirky ornaments from your travels or communal areas conducive to gathering for good conversation.

Holistic Tip
Change the Atmosphere

You can never underestimate the effect on body, mind and soul of serene surroundings. Keep it simple: with an aromatherapy candle, an essential oil burner, classical music or a roaring fire. You may even be amazed at the reaction of everyone else at home. We like our creature comforts and a calm relaxed atmosphere can set the scene for a chilled out evening for all the family. It will be worth the effort when there are no arguments at the family meal, and the children go to bed easily.

Once you have changed one room in your home, why not work on another one? Doing small steps will help you achieve your overall result and will also allow you to see the fruits of your labour. You could try moving your furniture to different parts of the room. Are there any corners or parts of the room that you don't use? Why not put a plant there or a lamp? Try and think about the space and how it is laid out. Is there a room that you would like to change the function of, for instance, a spare bedroom to a study. Think about it and discuss it with friends or family. As well as improving the function and feel of your home, it can also be good fun.

Geopathic Stress

In ancient times all churches, sacred sites and places of worship were built on 'ley lines'. These are energetic acupuncture-like lines in the earth, which indicate good energy spots. However, due to the plethora of machines, electricity pylons, electromagnetic appliances, in our modern world, negative energy spots can develop. These are places in our homes which no one uses or stays in for long, and they feel cold and uninviting. Usually, these areas are where dogs don't go to and cats love to sit in. The animals sense the energy here

– dogs avoiding it and cats neutralising it. I'm talking about a slightly negative energy that can be removed fairly easily.

Tune Into Your Own Home

We usually can 'sense' how we feel in a particular room fairly easily. Walk around your living space and note the places least used. Divert any geopathic stress by moving the furniture around into another configuration, placing plants or crystals (rose quartz is particularly good), in that part of the house until you 'feel' a change or warmth. Nine out of ten times this will suffice, if not then you might consider getting a geopathic stress expert in. They may use a simple audio device (Raditek), which makes a loud noise in affected areas or use an old fashioned method called divining. You may have seen pictures of people with divining rods looking for water. It is based on the same principle. They will advise on how to correct affected areas. The local health food store, phone book or internet will guide you to a reputable therapist.

Holistic Tip
Find Your Dream Space

Somewhere in your home is a place where you can be yourself totally. A place to be in the moment, drop your guard and dream big. Is it the bed, bath or conservatory? What comes to mind when reading this? Personally, I love to meditate and do my yoga on the upstairs landing, because of the early morning light and how it sets me up for the day.

Chapter 5
Work Life Balance

We all need balance in our lives between work, home, romance, family and socialising. When the balance goes and we feel less healthy, fit or relaxed we can then succumb to the effects of stress. When this occurs we need to look at our work life balance to see if it is out of sync. In our busy world we know that time is precious, and there will constantly be many demands on us. The best idea is to make your time both at work and home most effective, so you can sustain a good lifestyle that works for you, at each stage of your life. Remember, this will change constantly, as you age, so what works in your twenties will be different in your thirties, forties and so on. The idea should be to work less hours more efficiently than long hours exhausted.

If everyone works like this we are onto a winner. One person can make a difference and that person could be you.

In the Now

How often do we look at the big, scary picture thinking I'll never be relaxed, able to cope/lose weight/get fit? We tend to bring the past with us clogging up our brain with old hurts and mistakes. Let them go! We also try to live for a future better time. It might never happen. Just focus on the here and now, and what you can do at that moment, especially if you can feel your stress levels rising along with possible symptoms like, sweaty hands, fast breathing and racing thoughts. What to do? When we are relaxed our breath is always slow. The reverse is also true, so that if we breathe slowly – we will automatically relax. The old adage of "when stressed count to ten slowly", is using this wise principle. By the time we have got to ten, our breathing has calmed and we have now a chance to look at the situation in a new light.

Holistic Tip
How Do I Find The Time?

A good time to destress is when you come in from work after a busy day. If there are others at home, then tell them that you are going to take 15 to 20 minutes to yourself to unwind. You could use this time to have a soothing bath, or listen to relaxing music or to just breathe and have a little snooze to recharge your batteries. The first time you suggest doing these things expect derision or lack of understanding. That's okay, go ahead, and trust me in a few days they'll be asking when are you off to unwind.

A Really Tough Day
You have a choice: you can complain and resist the work you have to do, which will slow you down and

annoy you even more, or you can throw yourself 100 per cent into the tough day, but look forward to going home to your safe haven. I like to close my eyes and imagine that soon I will be on my comfy sofa with a warm rug to snuggle up in. Then is the time to plan a big treat. This may not necessarily be of the chocolate variety, but if it is go posh 70 per cent dark chocolate at least.

Emotional Release

If I feel stressed on the way home from work, I get a weepy, action or comedy DVD to cry or laugh away the frustrations of the day. I regularly let Daniel Craig, as James Bond, fight away my tensions, especially when he wears those small shorts! I once counselled a man who realised that he handled stress very differently to his wife. Eventually, together, they came up with a brilliant plan. He bought a set of his favourite comedies, and graded them according to his stress. So if his wife came back home and he was watching an episode of 'Fawlty Towers', she would know that he had had a tough day. However, if he was watching 'Father Ted', then she would know that it was a particularly stressful day, so she would head off for a night with the girls to give him some space. It worked perfectly for them, since he released his tension through laughter, and she knew non-verbally what was going on.

Sunshine Sheet

There is a really good visual technique that brings home exactly what you yearn for in your life. It is a fabulous way of literally seeing the balance you want in all aspects of your life. To start get a whole pile of old magazines, a scissors, glue and a large sheet of cardboard. For about an hour, flick through the magazines and cut out photos, images and even sentences that catch your eye. Try to choose ones that depict how you WANT to live your life in the not too distant future. It is often amazing how dreams you have held in your heart for a long time emerge naturally.

When you have all your cuttings, arrange them on the sheet of cardboard in a way that pleases your eye. Note that all aspects of your life are featured: work/study, family, friends, social life, personal development. Now this is a visual depiction of what you want to bring into your life. If you are single, you may have chosen a picture of a happy couple with children. If you are a homemaker, you may have chosen a happy fulfilled working woman with adult children doing their own thing. Now place

this sunshine (so called, as it should shine light into new areas of your future and make you happy to look at it), in a prominent area of your personal space. This may be your bedroom, so you see it last thing at night and first thing in the morning. It could be in a desk drawer at work or anywhere that you will see it, at least two to three times a day. Subconsiously, you are attracting this balanced future life into actuality. That may sound a bit airy fairy, but you would be amazed at its effectiveness. All I can say is: try it out for yourself and see.

The Magic List

It is a great idea to always make a list of what needs to be done in order of priority. Most of us do this at the start of our day, taking pleasure striking items off our list as the day progresses. The important thing to do is factor in break time and lunch time. Time to eat and digest your food, time to chat with colleagues; the important little habits we often forget to make and keep. How many times has the day passed when you realise you have had just a sandwich at your desk or even no lunch at all? We need breaks to give ourselves a rest and to rejuvenate for later tasks. A good change to make is the new habit of finishing the day by making a list for the next day. This way you don't have to attempt to try and hold any information in your head about work at home. If you do have a thought occur when you are at home, write it down immediately, and then forget about it. Remember, it is also a good habit to make lists for your home, again freeing up your mind from having to remember the minutiae of life at the office. The important thing is not to forget to factor in 'downtime' for yourself at home, even if it is only half an hour in the garden or on the couch watching a favourite television programme.

Holistic Tip
In The Mood

Imagine you wake up one morning and you're not in great humour. Your list that day might have two major tasks (of top priority) and three minor tasks (of lower priority). Rather than forcing yourself to do the main task, when you don't feel like it, tackle one of the short minor ones to 'warm yourself up'. This way you are doing something you don't mind doing, and since it is short, you will finish it quickly and feel good as you strike it off your list. By then your mood will have changed and you will be able to face one of the major tasks. You can also use the treat system here, where you throw yourself into the major task promising yourself a treat afterwards.

Body Clock

Some of us are night owls and some of us are morning larks. See if you can work out the time of day you are most productive. That is the time to schedule important meetings, write vital documents and do essential household tasks. When you have figured out the time you are not as productive, then do your filing, dusting or make some easy phone calls. If you are working as a team or family on a project, pool all the skills and talents, so that the right person is doing the right job on the team. If you like a particular task you will do it best. I work most effectively between 9.00am – 1.00pm. In the afternoons I like to do simple organisational tasks after my lunch, to give me time to digest my food. In the evenings after clients, I might answer some emails, but after 8.00pm I'm ready to chill. I never ever could study or retain knowledge after this time. This information really helps me plan my day. I tend to keep important meetings for mornings, when my brain is at its most alert and my energy levels are at their best.

Holistic Tip
Timesheet

If you have never used a timesheet it is a great way to figure out what you spend most of your time doing. In your notebook mark out a day in half hour time slots, and then fill in the time your jobs or tasks start and end, in the appropriate time slot, during a typical day. You may find that phone calls on a Monday morning are a waste of time, since people are busy at team meetings or sorting out their week, whereas in the afternoon it is easier to get them. You may be surprised to see how long you spend answering emails and making phone calls, so you might need to factor in more time to do this, instead of squeezing it into an already busy schedule.

The Unsustainable Hero

In a new job there is usually a three-month trial period when we are on our best behaviour, working fast and furiously. However, after this time, when we have secured the job, we need to go back to a normal level of work, which is sustainable, or else we will overwhelm ourselves and burn out. It is very possible to be superwoman or superman for some of the time but not all of the time. Are you still in this mode whatever your job is? Take stock now and learn to say no. Paul Newman, the actor, was reknowned for not giving autographs with his big twinkly blue eyes saying 'No' in the most gorgeous way possible. Nobody was ever offended by his refusal. Do you need to learn to say no gracefully too? This was a huge lesson for me, and one that really paid off in terms of my time and energy. You know what? The earth didn't stop spinning and, more importantly, my family, friends and colleagues still respected me when I said no nicely.

Holistic Tip
Family Time

Whether it is with a partner, family or friends we do need to factor talk time into our week. Many of us spend evenings at home, where everyone is busy at their 'own thing' and there is no meaningful conversation. Little children need small daily bouts of playtime, where they suggest the games and stories. Older children need weekly bouts of a longer activity. Friends and parents appreciate good conversation and perhaps a shared outing. We need to actually schedule these special times, rather than spending valuable energy thinking about when we can squeeze them into our busy weeks. In your notebook, figure out when you can arrange this time. You'll notice that you'll enjoy it much more when you have planned ahead, and are not stressed.

Yoga Woman

Usually people come to yoga class of their own volition. One particular evening, as I welcomed newcomers, a woman sheepishly handed me a piece of paper. "Here", she said, "I 'have' to do a yoga class". Fascinated, I asked her to explain, and she told me that she had been on anti-depressants, and recently went to get a new prescription. The old doctor had retired and his son had taken over the surgery. He asked her why she was on the tablets, and she explained that she started taking them when her mother died. The young doctor said how sorry he was to hear of her bereavement and depression. She assured him that she had fully grieved, since it happened five years previously. So, the young doctor then asked why she was still on the tablets. She told him about her part-time job, her six children and her busy lifestyle, then she zoned out, as he described various relaxation techniques.

She made her way to the local pharmacy and asked for the usual tablets, as she handed in her prescription. The baffled assistant replied, "I think you are in the wrong place, Missus". The piece of paper said, 'Try a yoga class'. Her husband encouraged her, and drove her to the venue.

Reluctantly, she took part and when we got to the relaxation part she fell asleep, snoring loudly – to the amusement of the others. At the end I encouraged everyone to do a bit of the breathing technique at home. She roared laughing telling us that was impossible, as she was so busy she didn't have a minute to herself.

The next week, she bounced into the class, so changed I hardly recognised her. She told us how the following evening, she explained to the family that she had to do 'homework' for the class. The children thought this was hilarious, as they were about to do their own, supervised by her husband. Up she went to the bedroom and did ten minutes of yoga breathing and visualisation. She prepared to go back downstairs and noted that silence reigned, there was not a murmur from the family, so she did another few minutes. After that she dusted off a book, she had never read, and enjoyed a couple of chapters. She ended by looking out the window at the spring flowers coming into bloom, before she returned to the family. The following night, to her utter amazement, a miracle happened, as her husband said, "Now, children, be good, your mother has to go upstairs to do her HALF AN HOUR's yoga homework." She was just about to say that actually it was only ten minutes, when it finally dawned on her that she had managed to invent free time for herself every day. That half an hour changed her world; she painted her toenails different colours, relaxed in hot baths and read library books, as she fantasised about what treats she could dream up for the next night.

Chapter 6
Confidence

'Confidence: a feeling of self-assurance arising from an appreciation of one's own abilities.'
Oxford Dictionary, tenth editon.

What actually is confidence? A state of natural belief in ourselves? An inner sense of calm and poise? The ability to mix easily in social situations? It is all of the these – and contary to what most of us believe – it is never too late to learn how to be confident. In an ideal world our parents, with their own confidence, would have taught us how to build our levels of it from babyhood. Most parents however, may not have a sense of it themselves, and even if they did, with the stresses and strains of life may not be in a position to pass this magical quality on to their children. The good news is that we can learn it ourselves at any age fully and completely. Confidence is like happiness – it is a state of being that you can nuture by adopting certain habits and daily rituals.

Building Confidence

The changes that you can make to build a state of confidence are simple. Never underestimate the power of a smile. Those less confident often marvel at people walking into new situations with their head held high. If you haven't picked this habit up from childhood, then the following is a technique that works very well. Most of us are drawn to people who appear confident, if you appear so then others will be drawn to you. Sometimes we worry about what to say, feeling that we need to have a witty, sparkling repartee to fit in. Often a few simple questions can get a conversation started.

Holistic Tip
A Confidence Building Habit

The next time you enter a new situation, try this simple suggestion. Walk into a room, as if you are about to meet someone you know, with your head held high and a smile on your face. Approach someone who looks familiar. Don't forget that most people like to talk about themselves, so all you have to do is come up with three questions that you are comfortable asking. Questions like: Who do you know here? Where are you from? What do you think of the event? You could also comment on the size of the crowd, the décor or anything else that comes naturally to mind. The other person will most likely appreciate you approaching them, and be glad of having someone to talk to. This technique may sound almost childish in its simplicity, yet to many it will be a huge step. However, the main point is that it is highly effective and can change how you act socially forever.

Self Acceptance

Acceptance of your body is a reflection of your self-esteem and confidence. If you view yourself as you think others view you, then you are setting yourself up for a negative way of looking at your body. Ideally, we should be working towards a sense of being comfortable with who we are. We also need to check in with close people, who we trust and are barometers of truth, to see that this self view is appropriate.

Remember that a dog will never be a cat and a budgie will never be a goldfish. So if your family are tall, big boned and well endowed, you are not going to have the figure of a nine-year-old boy, which is the infamous size zero.

Holistic Tip
Do Your Best

So often we beat ourselves up mentally and emotionally for what we think we should be doing, instead of just doing it. It is a good idea to have very simple healthy tasks in mind for the inevitable times when we feel despondent or inevitably 'fall off the wagon'. I like drinking a glass of water, stepping outside for a breath of fresh air, pottering in the garden, even just breathing deeply will do. Then you feel that you have recognised the start of a downward spiral, and are doing something about it by breaking the chain of negative thoughts. Don't berate yourself for the slip, just change the way you think about it and start the healthy habits again straight away.

Be Kind To Yourself

Most of us have heard of the biblical saying: 'Love your neighbour as yourself'. We take this to mean be nice to your fellow humans. Actually, what it really means is treat yourself as you treat others. I believe that this is one of the most difficult things to do in life, especially if you are an Irish woman. More than likely we did not have ideal role models in our mothers and grandmothers in how to look after ourselves, before we look after our loved ones. If they didn't have those role models how could they pass these skills on to us? If we want to be there for those who need us, then we need to realise that we are no good to anyone if we are tired, exhausted or have low energy.

Holistic Tip
Worst-case Scenario

How many times is our confidence effected by worrying about the outcome to a given situation? Instead of fretting, why not work out the worst-case scenario. Usually, it is not too bad and we could cope with it, which eases the way we look at the situation. So, say you were anxious about starting an evening course and lacked the confidence to join. Then the worst-case scenario is that no one would talk to you on the first night. You wouldn't feel great and you would probably either have to make the effort to talk to someone or leave the class. You might feel nothing ventured, nothing gained, so that if you decided to talk to others on entering the class then odds on the worst-case scenario would never happen. In other words, the small change it would require to talk sooner rather than later will really make a difference.

Find Your Passion

What excites you in life? What gets you up in the morning with a sense of purpose for the day? These might sound like strange questions. However, many people get to a stage in life where they are drifting along with no buzz in their lives. Boredom can be a real contributor to feelings of low self-worth.

You have so much time to mull over the aspects of your life you perceive as wrong, that you may be dragged down by a sense of inertia – a vicious circle. The key to finding a way out of this rut is a personal interest that captures your imagination.

If you can't think of anything, fine. A clue is some hobby you love to do. When we do these favourite things we usually lose all track of time, stop worrying and feel good afterwards. Can you remember something you enjoyed doing when you were younger, but feel you couldn't do now? It could be painting, acting, dancing or horse riding. As we get older, we sometimes feel that 'age' restricts us from joining in a particular activity.

If there is something you have always wanted to do, why don't you at least think about it, or discuss it with a friend or family member, who you feel will be supportive and encouraging. You never know, they might decide to join as well. Ladies, this is the reason many men have tool sheds, make Airfix models and tinker around with their car for hours. Gentlemen, now you know what we are doing when we knit, bake or indulge in some retail therapy.

Holistic Tip
Confidence Boosters

Sit down with your notebook when you have time, are fed and relaxed. Make a list of ANY time in your life when you felt more confident than usual. Now note what was going on in your life at that time. Who were you hanging out with, what were you doing, where were you living/working? Try to figure out what was the common denominator that contributed to your confident feelings at that time. You may find that you had more time or less time to yourself. Perhaps you were exercising more or eating healthier. Maybe you were in love with a supportive person who appreciated you. Once you have finished your list, figure out what are the key things that help you to feel more confident. Then one by one, slowly reintroduce them into your life.

Time Out

I know one woman who did a version of that previous exercise and discovered that she loved to soak in the bath, at least three times a week, as a way to unwind, destress and pamper herself. One day she and her husband decided to revamp the house, and took out their bath in favour of a power shower. From that day on she felt that her life took a turn for the worse. She felt irritable and couldn't understand why she didn't feel herself. Her confidence plummeted, as her sleeping pattern changed. To her utter amazement, she traced it all back to the lack of her bath – the symbol and means of her total relaxation. Personally, I would find it very hard to live in a space without a bath or a real fire.

Confidence Scoring

Give yourself a confidence rating from 1-10, where 1 is low confidence and 10 is high confidence. Most people are probably at about a 7. If your score is below this then you really need to look at this area of your life. You are more than likely underestimating your self-worth and achievements. Start by doing all the suggested tips and then redo the rating scale. I would say that your score will have improved significantly by then. If not, I suggest that a visit to a reputable counsellor or life coach is a good idea to get some professional help.

Chapter 7
Self-Care

In order to become aware of any aspects of our life that we would like to change or amend, it is important to look at our own care: self-care. Most Irish people don't have a good history of self-care. Many of our parents and grandparents were so busy just surviving that they may not have been the best role models. If anyone did take time out to look after themselves, they were often labelled selfish, immodest or vain. Now that people from other cultures are living in Ireland sharing our lives, home, school, work, college, etc., we have the opportunity to learn from aspects of their healthy outlook on self-care also.

Once we look after ourselves then we begin to value and respect, and dare I say it, love ourselves more. If we can love ourselves then we are in a better position to love others unconditionally. There is an Irish folklore riddle, quoted by the bards, to begin a story telling session, 'Where is the middle of the world?' The answer is: 'Here, where you are standing now.' The centre of our universe begins with us, and we really need to learn how to look after ourselves, especially if we want to take our place in the world.

Physical Self-Care

Have you ever noticed that when you feel fit and healthy, difficult life events don't effect you in the same way as when you feel out of condition? We have a physical body for a reason and we need to look after it daily. If we can maintain three hour long or six half hour exercise sessions in our week, which we can do easily then we are on a winner. We need to make sure to pick an exercise that we like, so we will actually do it. Walking is a classic execise, which can be done with a friend or partner for a chat or alone to chill out totally. Many people find swimming very therapeutic, and there are lots of local pools with open hours available to the public. Gym work can have a soothing rhythmic effect on your system, while keeping you trim and toned whether that be on strength training weight machines, cardiovascular equipment or a group class.

Regular Exercise

Any good exercise regime must be sustainable throughout our lives. If we played basketball and trained four times a week for hours in our 20s, will we be able to do this when we are 30, 40 or 50? Our bodies get used to exercise and when it stops or is drastically reduced, but we eat the same quantity of food, what happens? The weight piles on and our body tone is reduced. We need to maintain an easy level of exercise, which combined with good healthy eating, will sustain us throughout life. So we might be clubbing, playing squash and rollerblading at 20; doing aqua aerobics, pushing our baby's buggy uphill and walking at 30; salsa aerobics, yoga and hill walking at 40. The sport will change according to our lifestyle, but the amount of exercise will remain consistent.

Holistic Tip
Realistic Exercise Assessment

Write in your notebook which exercise makes the most sense for you to do at this stage of your life. If you feel overwhelmed by not having enough time, look at your daily routine and see if you could incorporate exercise into it. Could you cycle to work two mornings a week, thus making up an hour of exercise? Could you ask a colleague to go for a 30-minute walk with you during lunch? See if there are any gyms, swimming pools or exercise classes near your work.

For years I taught yoga and weight management classes five times a week. When it was a natural time for me to stop teaching these, I was 42, and within one year, I found I put on weight, mainly around my midriff. Not exactly enough for anyone else to notice – but I did. I had to reassess my exercise by starting early morning body conditioning and yoga classes locally, where I was the student. That tipped the balance and now all is well with my weight. The more we look after our bodies the easier it is to maintain good health and reap the benefits of looking our best.

Know Your Own Style

Now that you have started to look at getting fit and toning up your body, how about assessing your own style? Have a look through your wardrobe and note the clothes that you really like. Is it the fabric, colour or style that appeals to you? We can play up our good points with our clothes by getting to know what suits us. By becoming aware of our body shape and what flatters us, as well as knowing the colours that compliment us, we can save ourselves a lot of time and money. Then each season we can pick clothes that really look good on us. Remember that accessories are great for revitalising an outfit. By sussing out what is in the shops and choosing items that vaguely match from our existing wardrobe, we can, with carefully chosen scarves, belts and jewellery recreate the look for ourselves.

Experimenting with girlfriends is fun, as sometimes they can have a better sense of what might suit us. Doing your own version of a 'make over' evening is a great laugh, inexpensive and you can end up with a whole new look.

Skin, Hair and Make-up

As well as working on your wardrobe, why not take a look at your overall image? Assessing your skin care, hair and make-up, which can date you hugely. Changing even the colour of a lipstick can revitalise your make-up. I advise keeping your day time make-up natural looking, and adding something extra to your evening make-up to add that touch of sparkle.

Skin care is so important, and I like to stay natural by using products with essential oils, which enhance my skin and keep that youthful glow. Remember that as you grow older you will need to change your skin care to match your change in skin texture. If in doubt, seek advice, and try to remember to wear some type of sun protection factor (SPF) during the day – SPF 15 is a good start.

Emotional Self-Care

We need to realise that our emotions are there for a reason – to release tension and to own our feelings. They also indicate if something is wrong and help us to learn and grow. We need not be afraid to experience our emotions, both good and bad. Remember our friends and family know and care about us, so we can try to be comfortable with them, by letting down our guard now and then. Often we hold in our emotions, keeping a stiff upper lip and pretending we are fine. This will keep the family routine going but at what price? Our friends or colleagues will understand if we say something like, 'I feel a bit down today. I just need to relax for a while, and I'll be grand tomorrow'. We are letting them know that we aren't feeling great, that a little time-out will help and we will be fine again soon.

Holistic Tip
Treat Time

A good idea is to have some favourite treats lined up for your self-care. I love the concept of really nice treats to be 'cashed' in when you most need a pick-me-up. Ideal treats could be a massage, a hairdo, a cappuccino with your favourite magazine, a lie-on, the list is endless. Sometimes just the knowledge that you have lined up a treat will keep you going through a busy and stressful week.

The Gift of Time

Avoid over scheduling at all costs. Only do what you can reasonably manage in your given time. It is a great idea to always factor in extra time, and if you have some to spare – do nothing just enjoy the peace. Another good time tip is not to answer the phone during mealtimes – remember that's what answering machines are for. We all have things we would like to do in life and we always seem to put them on the long finger. In your notebook write out a wish list, as a start, and arrange a day out with a friend or a holiday or hobby around it. We really need to make the most of life, so don't let it pass you by. There are many exciting milestones in the first half of our lives, as we grow to adulthood. In the second half, many of us see our 60th birthday, retirement, old age and death as all that is left. So, we have to be creative and invent new milestones in the second half of life, as we are living longer nowadays than our ancestors. Long distance travel to relatives, a much wished for hobby, like painting, time to explore our beautiful country are all possibilities that might excite us in our golden years.

Holistic Tip
Time Out

A student of mine once told me that once a month, she took time out for 'Swimming in the Sea of Me'. This meant that she finished her work and household jobs, explained to her family what she was going to do and promptly took valuable time to just 'be'. Sometimes it was an afternoon in a gallery or a day at a Spa, other times a girly lunch. It depended on her mood on the day. What a wonderful concept!

Very Personal Therapy

I spend one day every six weeks in bed. Yes, I know it's totally indulgent. Now your mind might be in overdrive trying to wonder how I spend that time. It's simple: I lie on, read, snooze, then picnic in bed, catch up on day dreams, chat and perhaps wind up on the sofa watching a chick flick. Bliss! What is your version of time out? What do you do already that can be expanded on?

At Sixteen

My fabulously creative cousin, Fíona Ward, introduced me to the delights of the Porchester Baths in London, in the eighties. An old-fashioned swimming pool with sauna and thermal suites, it was the forerunner of the many Spas we see today. Every month a group of friends would meet to pamper ourselves, catch up on gossip and chill out. There was a core gang but we could bring others, who would come and go. One time this stunning woman arrived with long blonde hair and a terrific figure. We were all very impressed. As she prepared for swimming, she tucked up her mane of hair into her swimming hat, revealing large 'sticky out' ears. She then proceeded to undress, and we noticed, surreptitiously, very short, mottled thighs covered in cellulite. Of course, no one said anything. Later in the Jacuzzi, she asked if anyone had noticed her ears or thighs. We all fell silent. She told us that at the tender age of sixteen, she had realised that her ears weren't great, but she didn't have the money to fix them. She noticed that her thighs were not her best feature, and also saw that she had inherited them from her mother and grandmother. However, she was smart enough to know that her hair and her tiny waist were her best features, so she vowed then to play up her good points, and camouflage her ears and thighs. Her reasoning was that only her lovers, family and friends would ever see them and they, of course would love her as she was. There wasn't a dry eye, as we wept for ourselves, and the body bits we had agonised over for years. She set us free and we loved her for it.

Chapter *8*
Mind Health

Mental Stress

Does your head ever feel overloaded with worries and problems? Does it feel like there is not enough time to process all that is whirring around inside? Mental stress is often the worst type of stress. It can be very debilitating on your physical, mental and emotional well being. It can leave your body feeling exhausted and your nerves in shreds. When you are stressed, often a relatively simple situation, like a very busy day, can snowball, leaving you totally overwhelmed. This type of stress can effect your sleep patterns, your ability to cope and, subsequently, your important relationships. Most of us are aware of the 'Fight or Flight' reaction. In times of stress adrenaline kicks in and we either want to fight a situation or run from it. Often the reaction is one we would not do under normal circumstances. Our stress takes over, so we can't stand back and really assess what is going on, and think about how we really want to deal with it. In theory this is a short-term reaction to deal with the problem in hand, but we often get stuck in the reaction to the situation, replaying it over and over again in our heads.

We are familiar with the physical symptoms of stress: fast breathing, palpitating heart, sweating palms, flushed face etc. We don't associate mental effects often with stress: worrying, negative thinking, insomnia, inability to make decisions and lethargic brain. These are the silent insidious effects that can easily go out of balance and linger long after the stressful situation has passed.

Worry

I often think that worrying is a national past time, as so many people are effected by it. Contrary to the popular saying, none of us are 'born worriers'. It is a habit that we learn usually from one of our parents or close family. We may assume that that's what men/women/mothers/fathers do, and so copy the behaviour. Those of us who are worriers have amazing brainpower, but we are using it negatively rather than positively. If we can get an appreciation of that fact and turn it around, we can literally move mountains with our newly won positive focus. When we worry we deplete our energy reserves, so that if the event actually happened then we would not be able to cope with it in the best way possible. We need to be able to understand why we are worrying, resolve the issue or change the habit and trust that when the inevitable difficult situations in life occur, we WILL be able to deal with them.

Negative to Positive
There are three key steps to overcoming worry and/or negative or anxious thoughts.

1. Awareness
In your notebook write down when you are worrying and what you are worrying about. Make a list of the key regular topics, for instance, finance, work, relationship. Now you have something to work on to sort out the problems. If the problem cannot be dealt with on your own, you may need to seek help from trusted friends or a qualified and registered counsellor.

2. *Distraction*

Figure out some easy distractions that you like to do, as a way of occupying your brain when it is about to go into worry mode, for instance, listening to your favourite music, watching a comedy, phoning a friend. This can be a really key way to actively changing the habit – giving us something concrete to do that in itself is relaxing.

3. *Positive Self-Talk*

This is the really important step where we talk to ourselves silently working out if there is anything that can be done. If there is, do it. If not, there is no point in worrying. Talk to yourself, take a deep breath and rationalise. It is very important to keep a light sense of humour on this step. It is no good 'beating yourself up' mentally. I often think of American teenagers saying: 'WHAT am I like?', with their eyeballs rolled and their hands on hips. This image instantly makes me laugh, when I realise how ridiculous I am in ruminating on something that might never actually happen.

These three steps will take at least six weeks to put in place. For the first week only do step one. Introduce step two, and be as creative as you can in finding those simple distractions. Finally, getting to the final step is vital, as that changes how you think to a new and empowering way.

Holistic Tip
Distraction Tickets

Find a gorgeous box or bag – you could even decorate it yourself. Make this your distraction treasure chest. Fill it up with pieces of beautiful paper, detailing wonderful things for you to do that you enjoy when you are feeling low, worried or anxious. These could be simple ideas (meeting a friend, feeding ducks, going to the library) or vouchers for treatments or clothes. Then when you catch yourself worrying or thinking negatively, choose one of the pieces of paper and do whatever is on it, as a way to take your mind off the situation.

Negative Thinking

It is a human condition to make mistakes as a way of learning and moving on. However, since this is not necessarily taught to us by our parents or in school, many of us stay stuck in the shame, guilt or confusion which builds up every time a mistake occurs. Is it any wonder that eventually we get sick, depressed or anxious with such 'baggage' we can end up carrying around? These are symptoms our body and mind has of letting us know that there is something wrong and we need to deal with it. A good way to think about it is that our anxious thought is trying to help us have a good look at our life and lifestyle, to find out what is up and to do something about it. Life will always have ups and downs. There will always be more to be done. Once we accept that then we can search for ways to cope with the stress of it.

Holistic Tip
Mental Stress Relief

A healthy body is important but a healthy mind is essential too. An easy way to relieve mental stress is to think of some hobby or interest that engrosses you completely. Gardening, walking, knitting, listening to music, reading, or even watching your favourite soap opera can help clear the mind and rejuvenate the body. Watching a film or reading a book is great escapism, you become so caught up in the story-line that the problem or worry is relieved for an hour or two. Any pursuit that you love to do, which leaves you feeling relaxed and refreshed, is ideal.

Difficult Situations

A good way to cope with difficult situations is to know that tough times happen, so the healthiest thing to do is learn from them and move on. How many times do we wallow long past the 'sell by date' on certain situations? We can hold grievances for years, nursing the old 'she said/he did' scenarios, which, lets face it, will get us attention and a ready audience when we talk about them. However, we will remain stuck in that unpleasant situation giving our power to the person who hurt us.

Remember if you haven't moved on, there is something wrong and you need to figure out how to work through or around it. Sometimes the wisest route is to seek help from a qualified and registered counsellor or psychotherapist, so that you can understand what is happening and learn new life skills for the future.

A wonderful colleague of mine, from the US, had a great saying: 'Living well is the best type of revenge'. You can bet that the person who perpetrated the problem isn't spending time and energy thinking of you all these years later, but you are wasting valuable time on something that is now over. Time to move on.

The Inner Critic

Have you come across the concept of the 'inner coach/good angel' voice that urges you on to bigger and better things? Maybe. However, I bet all of us know intimately the 'inner critic/naughty devil' voice that constantly tells us that 'we are no good'. These inner voices are there for a reason. The critic will speak first, to remind us of previous situations, when we made mistakes or didn't have the 'bottle' to go for something. A very common scenario is where we hear our old teacher's/ mother's or father's voice in our head as our inner critic. In theory, we will listen and remember what not to do. Then the positive voice, the coach, will spur us on to overcome our shyness, reticence or whatever we need to overcome. Unfortunately, often the inner critic wins out and we get stuck and don't feel brave enough to act on what our inner coach has said. If we can acknowledge this inner critic voice and even soothe it, then we can move over to our inner coach voice, and act on its valuable advice. This takes a bit of time but is very achievable.

Holistic Tip
Getting Some Head Space

Daily relaxation will give you the necessary rest to get some perspective on the problem in hand. You might be an 'active' relaxation person, finding a long walk or a game of golf or even a spot of DIY can help. Maybe you are a 'passive' relaxation person, who prefers to let someone else do all the work, while you chill out being massaged or pampered in a beauty salon. It doesn't actually matter which method you use – as long as you get a chance to let your brain have peace and relax.

Bottling it Up

In Ireland we have a history of bottling things up. Consequentially, as a very successful defence mechanism, we developed the maxim 'don't be telling people your business'. Now our history has changed, yet in the national psyche, we often still retain the last vestiges of this habit, particularly if we are 40 or over. The younger generation, who have grown up in a different Ireland, do discuss their emotions with friends, often to the horror of older family members. The effect of this secrecy or holding in of problems is that it eventually has to come out some way. When it does, it is ususaly in the form of our body's weak point – red flag. This is individual to each of us, depending on our physical makeup, how well we look after ourselves and our genetic pre-disposition. It is fine to open up and show our vulnerable side.

I am a typical Capricorn, and due to my psycho-therapy and holistic training, I work out my problems myself in a practical way, mentioning to my husband what I am processing. Eventually my family see the solution, but rarely see me in the throes of a problem. Recently, I realised the effect of this: very few people see me in difficulties. In effect I was bottling up the emotional side of me, so that only I saw it. I was working it out but privately. I began to see the huge learning in opening up to others, particularly my family. This can be an eldest child syndrome, where we feel we must show only our positive side to those younger. By talking about my problems, asking for advice and working them out with trusted loved ones, I was learning and so were they. It was a win-win situation with much love, tears and laughter thrown in for good measure.

The Mentor Factor

In times of difficulty, it helps to use the mentor technique. This involves thinking of a mentor/wise friend/parent, who you rate and respect. It might be just one or perhaps a few people, your own personal team. When you are in the throes of the tough situation, in your mind ask, 'What would Mary/Joe do in this situation?' You might be very surprised at what you think they might say or do. Usually, it's along the lines of, 'You'll be fine, relax', 'Stop and think' or 'Calm down, think it through'.

Ten Minutes Moaning Then Action!

Of course, you'll want to talk about the problem and get it off your chest, but don't bore anyone by going on about it incessantly. Tell them for ten minutes, then let them know about your action plan to counteract it. If you feel angry or frustrated then work that out of your system. Tennis or squash are highly recommended! Remember, this also works if people try to 'dump their problems on you'. Laugh and explain the ten-minute moan then action technique. You must stick to it always, otherwise you are giving mixed messages. This means they learn that if they moan enough you will relent and listen – disregarding the ten-minute rule. It takes time and effort and energy to be consistent but it certainly works. It will take approximately six weeks for the moaner to get the message. Persevere!

See the Challenge in Every Problem

Here's an interesting way of viewing any problem – see if you can find the challenge within it. So you might like to know the art of delegating and with extra work now you have an opportunity to do that. This busy time means you could also accept the challenge of keeping your stress levels low, or perhaps changing the habit of worrying. Once you have looked at the problem in hand, break down the solution to manageable chunks and either delegate or do one every hour/day until the problem is solved. This will give you a sense of achievement.

Not Being the Best

We live in a busy, competitive world and striving for the best is often drummed into us from childhood. Now there is nothing wrong with aiming high – it's great but allow yourself to fall short too. Don't beat yourself up mentally, if you haven't achieved perfection, few people do. Take note: 80 per cent is terrific and most of the world runs on that level. Remember to praise and thank yourself for getting to 80 per cent also!

The Guru's Guru

In a remote seaside village lived a poor holy man and his students. Every day, the holy man filleted the fish he caught, giving the good pieces to his flock and making a soup for himself from the heads and leftovers. One of the men asked permission to visit the guru's guru in a neighbouring land. The holy man was delighted and gave his consent readily, asking only that the student requested any message his former master might have for him. Off set the student, and travelled many days, until he reached his destination. He noted the rich pastureland and abundant crops within the ornate gates of the guru's guru's house. He knocked at the door of the huge mansion, and was admitted by prosperous looking servants. The guru's guru and his very beautiful wife and children welcomed him into their happy home, where he stayed for a few weeks. Eventually, after learning much, he knew it was time to return, but he remembered to ask his guru's request first. The guru's guru paused and then said, "Tell, my former student, not to be so greedy." The student was amazed. How could the wealthy teacher give this message to his poor former student? What did it mean? He knew the message giver was a good, kind man, so he recognised that it came from the heart. When he reached home, his guru excitedly asked for his message, and with great reluctance his student delivered it. "Oh, my master, how observant and wise he is!", the holy man cried. To the utter astonishment of his students, their guru explained that every night after he gave them their fish, and sat eating his watery soup he begrudged them every mouthful. His guru sat in his palatial home thanking the Universe for his abundance, but not clinging to even one blade of his lush grass.

Chapter 9
Spirituality

Mind, Body, Spirit

We hear the word 'holistic' used a lot these days. Many of us aspire to live from a place where we look at life from a mind, body and spirit perspective. In reality, we do the mind and body piece but often leave out the spiritual bit. Change is a great opportunity for spiritual growth. I know that for years I felt that it was one area of my life I was going to seriously look at 'one of these fine days', but I never quite got around to it. Until, that is, something went wrong. In my case, my father passed away suddenly at 53 from a massive heart attack.

The Meaning of Life

Now there's a big question, perhaps the biggest question in life. Most of us consider this after the death of a loved one, a major life event or difficult economic times. We are forced to embrace change, and this is an important opportunity to regard problems as challenges to figure out what to learn from any given situation. This doesn't mean that we don't have our share of problems, but it does mean that they don't affect us in the same way. Personally, I also learned to ask for help. Initially from my husband, family or friends. I then became aware that in certain situations when nobody was around I found myself saying silently, 'God, help me'. It sort of blurted out when I least expected it, and I thought that now was the time to try to find out what I did or didn't believe in.

Personal Belief

We need to feel that we have a place in the world, that we are making a difference in our own way. This might be as a parent, worker or neighbour. Harness whatever religious or spiritual beliefs you have to help you live your life to the very best. Remember, there will always be people better off than you and there will always be people worse off, so comparing yourself to others is not worth the effort. We need to learn from each experience and then move on with that newly acquired knowledge.

Who is Running the Show After All?

With a scientific background from college days, an experiential route rather than an academic one worked best for me. I have tried many paths and if something didn't work for me then I didn't pursue it. If something did resonate with me, for example, yoga, meditation and shamanism, then I integrated it into my life. After many years of experimenting with different approaches, I now have an eclectic mix. I believe in God, not as an older man with a beard on a fluffy cloud, but as a divine spark in me and in everyone and everything. I believe we all have two sides to us: a positive good side and a negative shadow side. They are both important parts of us. We have a choice every moment whether to live from the positive and learn and grow or to live from the negative and stagnate. It is our choice and our choice alone. I also discovered that mentally beating myself up when I did go down the negative route certainly didn't help either. I just stopped, got its message, turned around and went back onto the positive track.

Spiritual Beliefs

I am very aware that my sense of the divine, which embodies both masculine and feminine, is personal to me. I respect everyone else's faith, whatever it is. I can completely understand why many people love the formality of a particular religion. Perhaps you might like to take some time to figure out what is best for you. If you know already, then celebrate that fact with prayers/intentions or thoughts of gratitude. It is a marvellous way to live when you can communicate with the divine, whatever that means to you.

In my clinic I see many clients with a wide variety of problems, and I encourage them to tap into whatever their spiritual beliefs are. It is fantastic when someone returns to the next session telling me that St Jude, their guardian angel or their granny, who passed away, has helped them with their problem. The main thing is to find out what works for you, and then focus on whatever can help you in your life right now. The power of prayer and spirituality is immense, but don't take my word or version of it. You deserve to find and relate to your own – whatever that might be.

Holistic Tip
Nature's Helping Hand

I find nature a great way to receive answers when I pray. Sometimes when I am feeling low and I see a tiny bud in the depths of winter, I know there is always hope even after despair. Try an experiment: when you next pray/set your intention, go out into nature and allow it to mirror back the answer to you. You can be quite sceptical doing this – you only need an open mind.

Help Your Dreams Along

Thirty years ago the majority of us prayed in a formal religion, 20 years ago many of us began to practise the power of positive thinking, 10 years later it was all about using our intent. Basically they are all the same principle. We need to work out what we need to live our lives in the best way possible, then ask whatever higher power we believe in to help. Finally, we need to hand it over and take action toward the outcome. There is no point in wasting time worrying about how it will happen. We can free up our minds and energy to enjoy life, while waiting for the intent to come about. It is about trusting that it really will happen. There is a great spiritual proviso that I use a lot and that is to ask for something 'in the best possible way for the highest possible good'.

A colleague once prayed for help in a centre she worked where the client numbers were down. Two days later, all the therapists were handed their notice! She was dismayed, yet trusted all would be well. A week later, she was invited to join a very progressive holistic centre where she could practise all her therapies, and sure enough the client numbers rose and rose. She needed to hand over the situation, so that the best possible scenario would pan out.

Holistic Tip
Sacred Living, Soul Moments

Make your life sacred. Every day you have the opportunity to make a heartfelt connection with others. A smile or a helping hand can send a message of hope, friendship and kindness to those we meet. The reaction will be immediate – a return of smiles and heartfelt gestures. Try it for about a week and see the effect it will have on your life. I call these special times of connection 'soul moments'.

Soul Moments

These are times of heightened awareness when we know we are living in the present, unafraid of the consequences, open to really allowing the magic of life to happen. I love to observe these happening all around me for my gratitude meditation last thing at night. They make my soul sing during the ordinary times of my day. When I am relaxed, I become even more aware of them. Then last thing at night I love to play these special moments over in my head, to give thanks and to help me sleep deeply.

A Favourite Soul Moment

I remember being stuck in an awful traffic jam down by the canal in Dublin. The driver in the car in front was literally thumping the steering wheel with road rage. To take my mind off the traffic and his negativity, I began to look around. I saw a young mother on her mobile pushing her little son in his buggy. Suddenly the little boy let out a roar, 'Duckies, duckies!' He was pointing animatedly to five swans majestically swimming in the water. His mum and many people nearby stopped what they were doing and revelled in his delight at the 'duckies'. My heart leapt to see the expression of sheer joy and wonder on his face, and his mum's evident delight and pride. Of course what happened next? The road rager turned to see what everyone else was staring at and smiled too.

Holistic Tip
Quiet Time

The Rosary is a fantastic meditation practice designed to bring you quiet time, at noon and six o'clock, with family, friends or community. In my case, somehow the meaning had been lost for the people I had asked or they thought I was too young to know. When I studied yoga meditation, I realised what the Rosary was all about. Depending on your religious upbringing, you might consider going back to some of the practices, rituals and ceremonies to have a second look at the original meanings. They may have a new significance to you as an adult or you may come to the conclusion that you now have new ways of taking the quiet time for yourself at a spiritual level. Your guardian angel childhood prayers may now be a visit to an integrated energy therapist, who works with angel guidance. Perhaps blessing yourself with holy water could be swimming in the sea regularly in the glory of nature.

Chapter *10*
Relationships

What are Relationships?

There are many types of relationships we can have over a lifetime and they all change constantly. We start with our parents or guardians. Then we have our siblings or cousins and neighbourhood friends. Our next tribe is at school, both primary and secondary. At this stage of our development, we probably have had deep relationships with a family pet, and know the heart ache when they pass away. In our teens, we move onto romantic relationships – don't we all know the trials and tribulations of these angst-ridden times! We begin to form friendships of a stronger nature, as we move into adulthood, now more aware of the sort of people we enjoy spending time with. Eventually, we may end up with a life partner and children of our own. At this stage we are experiencing the spiral of life turning full circle, because we now know what it is to be an adult, perhaps looking after children or caring for aging parents. Often this might bring feelings of understanding, especially when we realise what it is to parent or be a carer and have to assume responsibilities.

A Key Relationship

We often think of relationships as only with a life partner. However, the most important relationship we will ever have is the one we have with ourselves. This is the one that will inform the degree of our self-esteem and worth. Many of us reluctantly admit that we don't really like ourselves. Usually, what we don't like is the part of us that we judge in terms of what we feel other people think of us. We see our not-so-nice qualities, while often remaining blind to our good traits. We need to be aware that we have a shadow side, the part of us that we think other people don't see. If we asked our loved ones, they more than likely would tell us, in graphic detail, about our little idiosyncrasies and quirky ways. Yet they still love us. Ideally as children, we start to learn how to love and respect ourselves, which comes from watching our elders.

I often ask parents, 'How would you like your children to be when they grow up? Most answers are variations of 'self confident, independent, happy, social, responsible, easy going, hard working, loving'. My next question is the crux of the matter, 'Who do they learn all these magical qualities from and mirrors how an adult is when they live this way?' Ah, the penny drops, they realise that the best way we can teach our young ones is to be the best we can be, mirroring these important traits at all stages of our own lives.

Daddy's Girl, Mummy's Boy

Our relationship with our primary care givers is of vital importance to the partnerships we will form ourselves later in life. Our view of male and female in our formative years are the people we live with. For most of us, our gene pool has come from theirs, so we are a mix of them. Therefore, we may be more like one parent than another, which may mean that we get on better with one of them. In an ideal world we would 'click' with both parents equally, but that doesn't always happen. Since nobody really talks about this, we can spend a lifetime feeling slightly guilty about this common phenomenon. This is very normal, so it is nothing to worry or feel guilty about. Once there is respect and understanding then we can progress in life knowing that our children may feel the same about us. If a client comes to me with an issue about their romantic relationships, which never work out the first question I ask is, 'how do/did they get on with their father (if female) or mother (if male)?' I know the answer, there is usually a problem either of not getting on terribly well, so no respect, or getting on too much, so no one else could ever reach that high standard. If someone is adopted, then the same applies, but without the gene pool connection. If anyone is from a single-parent family, then the nearest male or female role model will be their view of male or female. This may be a grandparent or a step parent/partner.

Holistic Tip
Wearing Their Shoes

Sit down quietly at a time when you are well fed and won't be disturbed. In your notebook, write about your relationship with your main female role model. Allow the emotions to come whether tears, laughter or frustration. Write in a stream of consciousness style, letting the words flow into each other with no worries about spelling or punctuations. Now close your eyes, in your imagination literally put on this woman's shoes. What was her life like in the time she parented you? Was there a recession, were times tough? Was she a natural mother? Did she have support? Did she have any friends or did she have to resort to sharing, inappropriately, yet, understandably with each eldest child all her problems? This is a tough exercise to do but highly enlightening. Now go back to what you originally wrote and reread it, perhaps add to it. Finally, if even through gritted teeth, silently or aloud, if you are alone, forgive them for what they did or did not do.

This exercise helps you to move on and make your own relationships, with no energetic cords tying you back to this primary relationship that has now been resolved. When you are ready, do the same with your main male role model. The 'in his shoes' questions may be about work – did he like it or just do it to feed everyone and put a roof over your heads? What was his relationship with his father? How did he get on with his partner? You may be very surprised at the emotions that surface doing this exercise. It is powerful but very freeing.

Romantic Relationships

I'll refer to partnership relationships as 'romantic' to distinguish them from the other ones I've mentioned already. Haven't we all dreamt of Prince or Princess Charming arriving to whisk us off on their white charger? How can we attract the right partner or if we have already met them, perhaps we could do with a few pointers in living happily ever after? We are familiar with the concept of a soul mate – someone who we can connect with and learn from at a deeply, vulnerable level. However, how can our soul mate ever find us – if we haven't found our own soul? We all lead such busy lives that we sometimes forget to be, just 'us'. If we find out what we love to do and then thoroughly enjoy doing it, this will bring us to a place of inner happiness, which is incredibly attractive for others to see and so they may eventually be drawn to us as potential dates or partners.

Holistic Tip
Changing Chance

We plan our careers, where we live, where we go on holidays with precision, yet we often leave the most important aspect of our lives to chance. What sort of partner are you looking for? I'd say you have to think about that. Take out your notebook and write down a detailed list of who you imagine them to be. You should have a column for physical, mental, emotional attributes, as well as ones for hobbies, career, family values etc. Often in my clinic, clients say that they would love someone irrespective of job or whether they had a property. This is true, unless you are career orientated or want an equal partnership. Get the idea?

Shared Beliefs

A beautiful and talented friend of mine, Gina Mackey, knew that her life partner had to share her spiritual beliefs. She laughed that she wasn't a 'holy Joe', by any manner, but she wanted a life where she would marry her husband in a church, so they could bring up their children Catholic, and be able to deal with life's ups and downs with the guidelines of their faith. When she met her soul mate, he was so relieved, as he shared the same values, yet had been frustrated in his search for an ideal partner. Years later, they are very happy together and have three beautiful daughters, who share their beliefs.

A Home Run

So, now that you have your list, where does this type of person hang out? Many of us assume that we can meet our future partners in nightclubs, bars and parties. Most of these are loud, noisy places, where it is impossible to have a conversation. Of course you will see their long legs and smouldering smile, but will you be able to hear or know anything about them? You might consider going to places where you could meet a prospective soul mate as a friend first, for example a sport club or evening class. I'm a bit biased here, since I met my husband in such a class. It was love at first sight – I'm very happy to report! I was single at 36 years of age, as I knew that there had to be something worth waiting for that I had just never experienced. All those poems and books had to be right – I wanted to be swept away in a torrent of physical, emotional and spiritual love. My first thought when I met him totally surprised me. I knew I was HOME.

Equal But Different

Perhaps you have met the partner of your dreams and all goes very well for a few months or even years. Then certain 'situations' happen with alarming regularity. Men and women DO actually think differently. Let's imagine you come home upset after a really busy day. He is not telepathic, so you need to tell him gently that you want him to listen to you for 20 minutes or so. It's just listening, so he doesn't have to make suggestions and fix your problem. You could tell him that you are aware that he wants to watch the match in half and hour, but a cup of tea or a glass of wine together would be really nice. The situation may be reversed, for instance, when your man goes all quiet and needs some space. Don't assume that you have done something wrong. Go off and do other things, until he is ready to share with you. If he doesn't share with you after a few days, then there is probably something wrong between you. Take some quiet time together and listen to each other with no interruptions. Start your sentences with 'I feel … when you do … , rather than 'It's your fault that …'. That way both of you are owning your feelings and not blaming each other.

Miscommunication is not just about the difference between men and women. It is common in any relationship, including same sex couples. It is true that often the things that drive us mad about our significant others are the very things that we need to work on ourselves. No matter how amazing our romantic partners are they cannot make us happy. They cannot climb inside our heads and change our problems – we alone have responsibility for that. Happiness comes from within in the presence of supportive loved ones. Not all of us will have partners or children in life, but live very loving lives as 'professional' aunties, uncles, godparents, friends and/or pet owners.

Parenting
This is a huge life change that we often long for in life, but when we actually experience it we understand that it really is momentous. It's not just

the emotional roller coaster ride that parenthood is, but the realisation that we have less time for our relationship with ourselves and our partners. Each little smile and funny gesture melts our heart, but somewhere in the midst of it all we can get lost. The best place to start is caring for yourself. This may seem an odd one to begin with but children need content, positive and relaxed guardians. Many parents are stressed or burnt out, having put all their energies into caring for and attending to their children. The idea is to lavish some of the care and attention you give your children on yourself. Most of us want to provide praise, encouragement and rewards for our children, we also need to remember do that for ourselves and our partners.

Holistic Tip
The First Step

Take some time to write down in your notebook, what you feel are your needs and wishes as a person and a parent. This may seem like a strange request but it is a vital one. When you know what your needs are, plan a special time this week doing something you really enjoy that sustains them. Pick out some examples of when you felt you did well as a parent, and use them as resources when you are feeling low or tired.

Playtime

Often parents will do everything for their children except play with them. They will feed, clothe and provide brilliantly, but there is no time left to sit down and have fun in a relaxed way. Children really need active one-to-one and family playtime for their well-being and development. Play between parent and child is not only rewarding and enjoyable, but it also builds a close relationship, which forms a basis for solving discipline problems. It's easy to fall into the trap of correcting children when playing. For this special time go out of your way to tell them they are doing really well. Essentially it is all about being a good audience to children in their play, taking a great interest in what they are doing and providing lots of positive eye contact.

An Astonishing Truth

A couple I met from England, saved up each year and worked extra hours to afford to bring the family on a 'Continental holiday' every summer. For the last week, after the excitement of France or Spain, they would visit their relations in Ireland, who lived on a farm. Eventually all three of their children grew up to be fine upstanding citizens, who made their parents very proud. Both felt it was worth all the sacrifices and effort it took to give them the little extras in life, like their precious holidays.

One day, out of idle curiosity, at a family lunch, the father asked the three of them what was the best holiday they had been on and why. He and his wife smiled thinking of all their wonderful trips abroad. The first son raved about when his dad taught him to fish on the lake near the farm. Son number two replied that he, "loved when we fed the animals with you, Dad and Uncle Joe showed us how to fetch the eggs from the hens afterwards." Hmmm, no mention of any foreign place yet. Finally, their daughter, joined in, "My special memory is, Mum, when you helped me make my first apple tart, just like Granny's, with the little leaves of pastry on the top, and how we all ate it for tea." A little shocked, it took the parents a while to work out what had happened. They had loved the exotic nature of the foreign holidays, and chilled out completely. By the time they got to the farm in Ireland, they had the time and energy to be with their children, just playing, having fun and teaching them wonderful nature skills. It was a very interesting discovery.

Chapter *11*
Relaxation

Life these days can be quite stressful, not just at work but also at home and in other areas of life. Anxiety and stress can affect us all, but often in different ways. Although we are aware of it, most of us are not quite sure what to do about it. So here are some extremely simple tips you can try to help relax on a daily basis. When faced with a problem, we often immediately rush in our minds to the huge scary end result. This can be totally overwhelming and lead us to major stress, as we perceive too many changes that need to occur. We need to stop and think what can we do right now. That might mean finding out from someone the extent of the problem, listening to two sides of the story or just breathing deeply, to give ourselves space to think what to do next. We can learn to practice being 'in the now', experiencing how we feel right now in our body rather than rushing off in our heads to wild future scenarios. Ironically, staying with the panic or anxiety – feeling it and breathing through it will help hugely. This is where trust comes in, trust that the panicky feelings will go away after a few unpleasant moments and be released. Of course, if we bottle them up then they will come back when we least expect it.

Holistic Tip
Stress & Relaxation Triggers

This may be something you have never thought about: what are your triggers for both stressful and relaxing times? Think about the stressful triggers first, not the awful full-blown panic attack triggers, but the smaller signs. Usually it is something like sweaty palms, shortness of breath and racing thoughts. Now make a new list of the triggers of relaxing time. I find for me they are looking forward to events, being outdoors, being fed not stuffed, being in the company of loved ones, a good belly laugh. When you have written your relaxation triggers, look at them and see how you can incorporate them more into your routine.

A Classic Relaxation Technique

It wasn't until I started yoga breathing, in a local class in the early nineties, that I discovered that I didn't breathe properly. Frequently my breathing became very shallow, when I was stressed and sometimes I held my breath completely, especially when doing something new or difficult. My first taste of yoga breathing was three part breathing, where we divided our lungs into three parts: chest, rib cage and the lower lobes. We exhaled through the mouth, paused, gently pushed up the abdominal cavity (to create a vacuum effect in the lungs) and then inhaled deeply through the nose. I found this quite amazing. I loved the strong releasing feeling of exhaling through my mouth. I envisaged all the stresses and strains of the day or week leaving my body. The wave-like motion of gently raising the abdomen before breathing into the nose was a revelation. I loved the feeling, so primal, so deep! I imagined light and energy pulsing into my body.

For me the awareness of needing to do some yoga breathing either during a busy day or at my yoga practice in the morning is the first step. It does take at least 10-12 breaths to slow the breathing down. Usually what happens is that one breath is almost like a sigh, a release. Then I know I am starting to ease down into my body, tension will be let go and soon my mind will follow suit. I love the calm and peace that ensues. Bliss! Often when doing something tough, like hill walking, I would find myself automatically going into three part breathing – much to the amusement of my fellow walkers.

Many people are surprised to learn that you don't have to actually learn formal yoga Pranayama (good breathing in the ancient Indian language of Sanskrit) to do breathing techniques. However, for me nothing beats the community of being with like-minded people in a yoga class setting, with a reputable teacher you connect with.

The great news is that you can do it yourself by practising 10 to 15 deep breaths any time you feel stressed or need more energy. An ideal time to do your breathing practice is just after you wake up, especially if you are the type of person who immediately starts to stress and worry about your day. Some people find this marvellous to do when they come in from work in the evenings to let the day 'go' and prepare for the evening ahead. Last thing at night in bed is a terrific time and ensures a good night's sleep. This is particularly good, if you find you toss and turn or wake up in the night. It is the regularity of the technique that works the magic – the breathing itself is simple to do. You will be amazed at how a short breathing practice once a day can change your world. Many women have found the technique useful to do during labour, as it helped them manage their pain control. It is also good for general pain relief.

Holistic Tip
Three Part Breathing

A very easy way to calm the body and mind

is to breathe *VERY SLOWLY*. It is the basis of yoga, t'ai chi and pilates, and works very effectively. This technique is called three part breathing. Imagine you are dividing your lungs into three parts – the upper chest, the ribcage and the lower lobes (sitting above the diaphragm).

1. Sit up straight, with your lower back against the chair, feet on the floor or lie down.

2. Exhale deeply and slowly through your mouth (cooling).

3. Push up/out your abdomen, which causes your diaphragm to lower creating a vacuum in your lungs.

4. Inhale slowly through your nose, as the vacuum brings the breath into your body.

5. Feel the breath rising from the lower lungs to the ribs and chest.

6. Do this 20 times to send a simple message to the brain via the nervous system – 'I want to be relaxed right now'.

Use Your Imagination

There is a really nice way to relax yourself or nod off to good quality sleep, which will leave you refreshed for the day ahead. Visualisation is all about using your imagination to bring you to a place of deep relaxation. You may sit in a favourite chair or lie down on a sofa or use your bed. Make sure you won't be disturbed for 10 minutes up to half an hour. With your eyes closed, start to visualise a favourite beach, garden or forest, just as though you were looking at a DVD. I am guessing that you have chosen a place you like to be in, so there will probably be a smile on your face by now. It is easy to focus on things we like, so any problems or worries will be forgotten, as you bask in that special place or memory. Many people find that a relaxation CD helps to get them started. So they listen to someone else's voice describing a peaceful and relaxing setting. I recorded my own relaxation CD called 'Quiet Time', as many of my clients wanted a voice that they were familiar with. I found this very helpful myself when I was starting many years ago.

Holistic Tip
Visualisation

1. Sit or lie down, perhaps with a blanket or shawl to keep you warm.

2. Close your eyes and relax your body, as much as you can.

3. Pick a favourite place to be in, for instance, a forest, in the garden, a paradise island etc.

4. Go through your five senses and really imagine you are there.

5. What do you see, hear, feel, taste and smell?

6. Lose yourself for five minutes in a total fantasy, while you escape from reality.

Meditation

So you may be thinking that this is some strange Eastern esoteric stuff that is not for you. Bear with me, as we look at what it is and then bring it into an Irish context. Meditation, or mindfulness, is simply a technique to bring your mind from a busy to a relaxed state. It consists of many easy focus points that allow your thoughts, particularly the racing ones, to settle. In India, where chanting is part of the culture, people get up at 5.00am in the cool mornings and chant cross-legged. This is not only part of their daily spiritual routine, but it also sets them up to start their day in a more relaxed and energised way.

So, how could we translate this principle of this to something familiar and easy to do? What type of things do you like to think about naturally? It could be something that you would look forward to doing? For me, it is thinking about loved ones, remembering great holidays and special occasions. This probably sounds very familiar, because, of course, visualisation and also breathing techniques come under the umbrella of meditation. So, when I need time out I start with some breathing then visualise a lovely memory or beautiful place to be in. When you first start your mind will wander away, that is only natural. Instead of beating yourself up for 'not meditating correctly', gently keep bringing your mind back to the focus you have chosen. It does become easier with time. My first meditation class cleverly taught us to sit for two minutes, then five minutes and suddenly we were there for 20 minutes and then it seemed easy.

Active meditation is doing a beloved hobby or interest, so you lose yourself in the pleasure of the activity. Make sure you do your favourite pastime at least once a week, as part of your relaxation 'tool kit'. You'll feel the benefits in a short period of time.

Holistic Tip
Mindfulness Techniques

- *Lie or sit down, close your eyes and think about one of the following.*

- *Your favourite person. Imagine them smiling, happy and in great form.*

- *Your breathing. The flow and ebb, as it gently expands your abdomen and your chest.*

- *Your favourite place to be — it could be on the beach, in a forest, your best holiday.*

- *You! Visualise yourself well, happy, pain free and in great form.*

- *You may use a relaxation tape or your favourite music to help*

Affirmations

We often have worries or anxieties that repeat in our heads causing stress and strain. Affirmations are an easy and highly effective way to get the worry out of your head and give yourself the soothing quality of positive self-talk. An affirmation starts with the word 'I', so it's personal. The verb is always present tense, to send a positive command to the brain. Finally, it is a gorgeous antidote to the worry. If you constantly think 'I'm always stressed', then the corresponding affirmation would be, 'I am calm and relaxed'.

When repeating it in your head sometimes it helps to 'sing' it to a favourite tune or emphasis a different word each time. You are distracting yourself by focusing your mind on a feel good sentence. Once you figure out any repetitive worries then you can invent affirmations to counteract them.

Totally Original Relaxation

This story makes me laugh so much. When I went to Saudi Arabia to be Princess Noora's relaxation therapist and yoga teacher, my sister, her French husband and their two gorgeous little toddlers moved back from France and stayed in my house, in Dublin, while they were looking for their own place. It was a time of great change for them all: new country, new culture, new surroundings, new routine. It was an exciting move and one they all welcomed, but change, as we all know, can be unsettling.

A few times my sister noticed that Jack (aged five) and his sister, Emily (aged three and half), were very quiet, and went to look for them. As she called their names they would appear suddenly, looking very mischievous. Eventually, she discovered that they were hiding under the stairs, where I had pinned up a beautiful llama rug that she and Pierre had brought back from a trip to South America, with the image of a llama woven into the skin. Jack and Emily used to take a break in the cool, semi dark with their new friend Coco (a French nickname for a horse). How inspirational!

Conclusion

I hope you enjoyed reading this book, and will begin to achieve some of the simple practical steps to *Change a Little to Change a Lot*. I have had great fun writing it and sharing my experiences with you. There is no magic wand or special formula – this book does what it says on the cover.

At this stage, I'm suspecting that you have a list of possible little changes lined up to start the ball rolling. In fact, I'd say you have already started, as you read through the chapters, making a mental or written note of some of the changes you might make, especially the ones that grabbed your attention and were relatively easy to do. Good, well done! The idea is that you use this book as a 'dip in' guide, now that the first read is over. When you have the first small change, as a tried and tested habit that has become part of your daily routine, you can return to the book to choose your next tip. I suggested at the start, that you write down the various exercises in a fancy notebook. Why not make a list in order of priority of the changes you want to line up for the next few months?

I suggest something like:
• Drink more water
• Add in an extra hour-long walk during the week
• Keep a food diary for five days
• Spring clean a room
• Make a sunshine sheet
• Spend time in nature
• Spend more time with close friends and family
• Listen more to my 'inner coach' and not my 'inner critic'
• Share any worries with a trusted friend

I imagine you'll find favourite chapters on topics that interest you more, since they probably relate to the areas in your life that you feel need the most change. Remember to take it easy, and only do ONE small change at a time. Old habits die hard, and we may still be hardwired to try valiantly to change a lot in one go. If there is one thing and one thing alone, I hope you have learnt from this book, then it is to keep the changes small, regular and achievable.

Do keep a light heart and a sense of fun, as you put these changes in place. Think of me and my mental image of the teenager with attitude and that gorgeous self-effacing exclamation of, 'WHAT am I like?!', when, inevitably I fall off the wagon, dust myself off and start all over again. Not as before, beating myself up mentally, but with laughter and a nod in the direction of my 'inner coach'.

Let me end with a favourite heartfelt story: Once upon a time there was a very stressed woman, whose family and friends advised her to take a break, since her symptoms were getting worse and they were concerned about her. She went away for the weekend, and ended up on a deserted beach. As she walked along, her head still whirling with negative thoughts and worries, she struggled to figure out how she could possibly even begin to change her life. She couldn't see the seagulls wheel across the blue sky or hear the soothing waves lapping on the shore. Eventually, she did notice a figure in the distance, making what looked like see-saw movements back and forth. Out of curiosity, she walked closer and saw a little girl surrounded by hundreds of dying starfish washed up on the sand. The little girl was reaching down, gently picking up a starfish, and leaning forward to put it carefully back in the sea. When the woman arrived beside her, she spluttered: 'What are you doing? This is crazy, there are so many of them, you can't change anything'. The little girl looked up at the woman, reached down, picked up, yet another, parched starfish and as she released it back to the water said, 'Ah, missus, sure I made a change for that one.'

May all your starfish end up back in the water, one by one by one.

Daily Health Checklist

Let's face it, we spend inordinate amounts of time thinking about what we should, and shouldn't do, to improve our health. Just imagine if we could harness all that valuable time to spend on ourselves with heaps of fabulous energy to go with it? Wouldn't we all be different people? Often we look at the big overwhelming picture; wanting to lose a stone in weight, run a marathon or change our whole wardrobe. No wonder we don't do anything about it. It seems like far too much work! So, what I'm suggesting here is we take one step at a time, with a simple daily health checklist that is manageable. We could have a routine for a normal day and even a reduced version of it for a busy day.

Exercise

Let's keep this very simple with a routine that we don't waiver from.

1. One stretch when we get out of bed. Pick a

manageable one you have learnt at a reputable class or from a physiotherapist.

2. Walk up stairs instead of taking the lift.
3. Walk to the local shops instead of driving.
4. Take a walk at lunchtime around the block.
5. Here's the biggie – exercise for an hour, three times a week. You can vary the type from a formal class to cycling to swimming etc.

On a very busy day do 1, 2 and 3. You'll notice the difference in less than a week. Within a month, your body will start to tone up and you might even lose weight.

Relaxation

Believe it or not, relaxation is a necessity NOT a luxury. We do need a balance in our lives to calm those nerves and soothe the system.

1. Do 10 deep breaths before you get out of bed, to prepare you for the day in a relaxed and calm manner.
2. Focus on what you do when you do it. It's called 'Being in the Now', and it means that your mind is not distracted by what comes next or what went on before.
3. Take two to three minutes time out to daydream; you could do this waiting to collect the children

from school, in traffic jams or a supermarket queue. You could even fantasise that you are some place exotic!
4. Play some soothing music during the day – Lyric Fm works a treat for me.
5. Each evening treat yourself to some 'me time' – a favourite TV soap, a long bath, a good book. Doesn't that all sound easy enough? On a busy day do the breathing from Tip 1 all the time.

Holistic Healthy Eating

1. Drink at least the equivalent of two small bottles of still water per day.
2. Have only three cups of tea and coffee a day, and savour those. Any more and you can't be getting enough water into your system.
3. Try a good brand multivitamin for one month, and see how your energy improves. The state of your fingernails will tell you if they are working. Your local health food shop will help you choose the best ones.
4. Eat one piece of fruit before a meal to aid digestion and weight loss.
5. Eat slowly. Take note: most indigestion is caused by eating too fast when you are stressed.

On a busy day do 1 and 3. Although, 5 will help calm you down as well.

A Good Source of Reference

Your local health food shop is a great place for health information, as the people who work there have a wealth of information about what is stocked in the shop. They can advise you on nutritious organic food, recommend vitamins and give advice on a myriad of healthy ways of being. It is also a fantastic reference point for local health information and yoga/pilates/exercise classes and events.

Remember to be realistic. We have all, at some point, radically changed our eating and exercise habits for a week or a fortnight, only to give up, as it is too hard to maintain. It is better to put a few simple healthy habits into effect and incorporate them into your daily schedule, so that they become second nature. It's not necessarily how much you do, but the length of time you can sustain it. Good luck and enjoy it! You'll reap the benefits within a week, and in a month you will be glowing with health and vitality.

Karen's website address is
www.karenwardholistictherapist.com

Recommended Reading

1. *The Health Squad Guide to Health and Fitness*
Karen Ward, Paula Mee, Padraig Murphy, Onstream Publications Ltd (Cork, 2005).
This was my first book, written with my *Health Squad* buddies, and photographed in Kelly's Hotel in Rosslare, where we are hosted by the inimitable Bill Kelly, twice a year to 'health squad' the guests.

2. *Brighid's Healing: Ireland's Celtic Medicine Traditions*
Gina McGarry, Green Magic Publishing (England, 2005).
This book was written by my inspirational Herbalism teacher, Gina McGarry; a sister in Brighidhood.

3. *Hollywood Legs*
Pat Henry, Marino Books (Dublin, 1997).
Pat is a terrific colleague, who I had the pleasure of working closely with a few years ago.

4. *Tending To Your Inner Garden: A Woman's Journey Towards Wholeness*
Catherine Maguire, Hunterhouse (California, 2009).
Catherine is a fellow Goddess of wild exuberance and earthy passion.

5. *Beyond Survival: Living Well is the Best Revenge*
Yvonne M. Dolan, BT Press (London, 2000).
I met Yvonne at her amazingly frank and original workshop; organised by my brief therapy group pals, Brendan Madden, John Sharry and Melissa Darmody.

6. *Parent Power: Bringing up responsible children and teenagers*
John Sharry, Family Matters series, John Wiley & Sons Ltd. (London, 2002).
A wonderful colleague, John developed the ground-breaking 'Parents Plus' programme (video-based parenting guides).

7. *Parents Plus early years programme:*
John Sharry, G. Hampson, et al. Parents Plus, c/o Mater Child and Adolescent Mental Health Service, Mater Hospital, Dublin 7. www.parentsplus.ie
A video-based parenting guide to promoting young children's development and preventing and managing behaviour problems.

8. *Simple Abundance: A Daybook of Comfort and Joy*
Sarah Ban Breathnach, Bantam Books (Great Britain, 1995).
My godson, Jonathan Sargent, gave this fantastic book to me, with a little help from his amazing mum, Alison.

9 *A Day Called Hope: A personal journey beyond depression*
Gareth O'Callaghan, Hodder and Stoughton (London, 2003).
A book I often recommend to clients, for its clear and simple message – there are ways to learn to cope with depression, and to live a really good life afterwards.

10. *Life and How To Survive It*
Robin Skynner and John Cleese, Vermillion, Random House (London, 1997).
Comedian John Cleese and his pal Robin Skynner, a medical doctor and psychotherapist, teach a lot in their hilarious and apt portrayal of life.

11. *The Complete Illustrated Guide to Feng Shui*
Lillian Too, Element Books (Boston, 1996).
An easy to understand reference to Feng Shui.

12. *Colour For Living: How to Change your Life With Colour*
Tina Dunne, Merlin Publishing (Dublin, 2008).
I was honoured to be asked to launch Tina Dunne's fascinating book.

13. *Quiet Time – to relax, renew & restore*
A relaxation CD with Karen Ward's voice talking you through breathing and visualisation techniques. It is available through Karen's website: www.karenwardholistictherapist.com

Notes